𝓂𝓁

15 APR 2000 ◇

Error Detection Circuits

Michael Gössel

Max Planck Society Fault-Tolerant Computing Group at the University of Potsdam

Steffen Graf

Computer Systems Services, Chemnitz

McGRAW-HILL BOOK COMPANY

London · New York · St Louis · San Francisco · Auckland
Bogotá · Caracas · Hamburg · Lisbon · Madrid · Mexico · Milan
Montreal · New Delhi · Panama · Paris · San Juan · São Paulo
Singapore · Sydney · Tokyo · Toronto

Published by
McGRAW-HILL Book Company Europe
SHOPPENHANGERS ROAD, MAIDENHEAD, BERKSHIRE, SL6 2QL, ENGLAND
TEL 0628 23432; FAX 0628 770224

British Library Cataloguing in Publication Data

Gössel, Michael
  Error Detection Circuits
  I. Title II. Graf, Steffen
  621.39'5

  ISBN 0-07-707438-6

Library of Congress Cataloging-in-Publication Data

Gössel, Michael.
  Error detection circuits / Michael Gössel, Steffen Graf.
    p.   cm.
  Includes bibliographical references and index.
  ISBN 0-07-707438-6
  1. Electronic circuit design.   2. Error-correcting codes
(information theory)   3. Fault-tolerant computing.   I. Graf,
Steffen.
  TK7888.4.G59   1993
  621.39'5--dc20   92-31694
                                                                                          CIP

12345 CUP 96543

Typeset by P & R Typesetters Ltd, Salisbury, Wiltshire
and printed and bound in Great Britain at the University Press, Cambridge

Rhao

CONTENTS

FOREWORD

Development of high-density low-cost integrated circuits has made on-chip error detection techniques commonplace. This book by Professor Gössel and Dr Graf is an outstanding first-time survey of various techniques proposed in diverse literature over more than thirty years. The book develops the basic theory in a systematic way, written in a manner not only useful for students of the subject, but also equally valuable for practicing engineers. The examples and exercises make this a valuable stand-alone text, excellent supplemental reading in a graduate course in fault-tolerant computing. Also, it provides an extensive list of references from both traditional western literature and important non-traditional sources. Thus, this book can serve as a valuable source of information for researchers in fault-tolerant computing and for VLSI designers.

Professor D.K. Pradhan
Texas A and M University

PREFACE

This book describes, for the first time, how an optimal error detection circuit can be designed systematically for an arbitrary combinational or sequential digital circuit. Here the error detection circuit detects the errors according to the error model chosen by a designer.

It is shown how the design of the optimal error detection circuit can be provided by optimization of a partially defined Boolean function or of a partially defined automaton. Methods and algorithms for the solution of these standard problems of circuit design are well known and can be implemented on computers. In the case of sequential circuits, the known algorithms for state reduction have to be used to optimize a partially defined automaton which, before the optimization, has only as many states as the circuit to be monitored. This enables the computer aided design of an error detection circuit, provided the computer aided design of the circuit to be monitored is mastered in terms of expenditure.

The problem of reasonably using a given number of gates, e.g. of residual gates in a gate array design, for error detection can be solved by the methods described in this book. The restriction of the error model to the most important, or most frequent, errors or a delayed error detection provides a reasonable error detection circuit with the available number of gates.

Error detection circuits are very frequently published only as patents. Therefore in the first chapter we have tried to review the patent literature, which has not been summarized elsewhere in such an accessible way. To give as clear and interesting an example as possible, in the second chapter we chose binary adders with different error models. It is shown that the overhead for error detection varies, depending on the error model, between 100 and 15 per cent of the size of the circuit to be monitored. The third chapter requires some patience in systematic reading, which in our opinion will pay off, especially if you want to carry out a computer aided optimum design of sequential error detection circuitry by the methods presented in the fourth chapter.

In the Appendix we show how the error model of a circuit is derived from component errors of subcircuits.

The methods we have described in this book will be useful to the engineer designing or using fault-tolerant circuits, to the computer science student interested in prospective hardware developments and to the scientist concerned with reliable and fault-tolerant computing.

It is a great pleasure for us to thank Prof. D. Pradhan, University of Texas, and Prof. C.R. Jesshope, University of Surrey, who have given very friendly support to the English edition of our book published by McGraw-Hill. We also thank Prof. E.S. Sogomonyan, Moscow, for his interesting remarks. The book was translated by B. Simon of Berlin and C. Sutton of Guildford. The diagrams were prepared by Mrs D. Naydowski. The text was considerably improved by the suggestions of the reviewers. We are grateful to all of them.

We thank Mrs G. Lagowitz for her excellent cooperation in the process of completing the manuscript. A final word of thanks is given to the McGraw-Hill staff, especially to Camilla Myers, Liz Nemecek and Andy Ware, for their patience and help in publishing this book.

ONE

INTRODUCTION AND OVERVIEW

Error detection circuits are used to monitor circuits for errors occurring during their operation (on-line monitoring). This must be distinguished from testing a circuit, where special predetermined inputs, so-called test sets or test sequences, are applied in order to test the correct circuit layout and localize errors that have occurred.

We shall deal exclusively with on-line error detection. The problems of testing are described elsewhere, for example in the books by Breuer and Friedman (1976), Roth (1980), Bennetts (1984), Fujiwara (1985), Lala (1985) and Wunderlich (1991). The interaction between on-line error detection and testing is dealt with specifically in Sedmak (1979), Parchomenko and Sogomonyan (1981), Fujiwara *et al.* (1984), Litikov and Sogomonyan (1985), Speranskij (1985), Rao and Fujiwara (1989) and Sogomonyan and Gössel (1992), and a general survey on fault tolerant computing is given in Pradhan (1986).

The known methods of error detection can be loosely summarized into the following groups:

1. Modifications of duplication and comparison
2. Application of codes
3. Algebraic methods
4. Detection of sequence errors

Such groups are to some extent arbitrary. It is not always true to say that a given solution fits neatly into any particular subdivision. These groups are, however, reasonable as a rough guide to aid understanding of this section only, and it is assumed that readers will go to the more detailed references if they wish to pursue any particular topic in greater depth.

Although we take account of as much of the patent literature as possible, we are not able to do this completely. This is particularly so with respect to the rapidly increasing Japanese literature which, without knowing the Japanese language, can only be traced by considering the relatively small number of patents applied for within Europe and the United States.

Many interesting examples of error detection circuits and heuristic solutions are known. However, until now no systematic method that is well adapted to the technical fault model has existed for the design of error detection circuits for random logic. Such a theory will be presented for combinational circuits in Chapter 2 and for sequential circuits in Chapter 3 of this book.

1.1 MODIFICATIONS OF DUPLICATION AND COMPARISON

1.1.1 Duplication and Comparison

The method of circuit duplication and of comparison of the sets of outputs is basically the simplest method of error detection. The principle is shown in Fig. 1.1. The circuit S is to be monitored for correct operation. To this end the circuit is duplicated by a parallel connection of two identical circuits S, whose outputs y_1 and y_2 are compared by a comparator, COMP. In the case of $y_1 = y_2$ the comparator output is 0 (no error) and in the case of $y_1 \neq y_2$ the output signal is 1 (error). If y_1 and y_2 are binary quantities, then the comparator is implemented by an EXCLUSIVE-OR (XOR) circuit.

This technique can easily be applied to almost all circuits. Moreover, it has the advantage that arbitrary malfunctions, provided they occur in only one of the two circuits, will be detected. A disadvantage of the method is that, for the time being, the full error-detected circuit is more than twice the size of the original circuit S.

Thus the circuitry shown in Fig. 1.1 produces about twice as many errors as those that actually occur in the circuit S because all of the errors occurring in the parallel connection of the two identical circuits are indicated. If both of the circuits S in Fig. 1.1 are defective in the same way as, for example, in

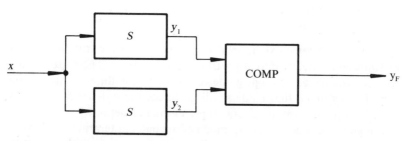

Figure 1.1 Duplication and comparison.

the case of design errors, then no error will be indicated by duplication and comparison.

If the circuits are produced as highly integrated circuits the number of faulty circuits is proportional to the chip areas required. Here a circuit duplication, and hence a doubling of the required chip area, leads to an increase in the percentage of faulty circuits produced and thus the yield of good circuits is decreased. Even if enough chip area is available, the duplication and comparison method may well give rise to considerable extra cost.

Since the method of duplication and comparison is simple it is extensively used as it is or in a slightly modified form. On the other hand, the above-mentioned disadvantages are the reasons that more sophisticated methods have been developed for special circuits better adapted to specific functional errors and technical faults. To give the reader some impression of the wide range of applications for the method of duplication and comparison and its variants, we will now describe different examples of this method.

1.1.2 Two-Rail Logic

A special variant of error detection by duplication of the circuits and comparison of the outputs is so-called two-rail logic (Sellers *et al.*, 1968; Siewiorek and Schwarz, 1982). Here the original circuit and its duplicate are designed as a logic including inverse outputs, so that in the overall circuit all signals always occur in both the proper and the inverted forms.

At the corresponding points, the error detection circuit in each case operates upon the inverted signal of the original circuit. At the same time all of the components are replaced in the way shown in Table 1.1. Clocked storage elements are replaced by elements switching with the inverted clock.

These measures slightly reduce the amount of circuitry that is required when compared to the original form of duplication and comparison, without impairing the error detection properties. This improvement is due to the fact

Table 1.1

Gate type of original circuit	Gate type of error detection circuit
AND	OR
OR	AND
NAND	NOR
NOR	NAND
XOR	/XOR
/XOR	XOR

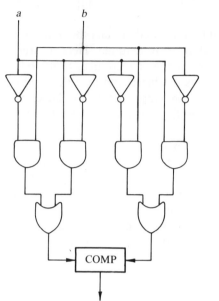

Figure 1.2 Duplication and comparison of an XOR circuit.

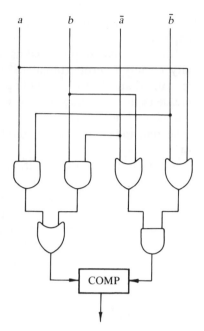

Figure 1.3 Monitoring of an XOR circuit by two-rail logic.

that all inversions can be implemented as a simple crossing of wires between the original circuit and the complementary circuit duplicate.

Figures 1.2 and 1.3 show a comparison between the monitoring of an XOR circuit by duplication/comparison and two-rail logic, respectively. AND, OR and NOT gates were used in the design of the circuits. The use of the two-rail logic saves the four NOT gates required in Fig. 1.2. The outputs have to be compared for equality in the conventional duplication manner and for inequality if the two-rail logic is used.

The advantage of a lower circuit expenditure for the two-rail logic is set against the disadvantage of additional design expenditure for the complementary circuit. This is a typical problem in the design of on-line error detection circuits. The search for advantageous error detection circuits frequently requires a compromise to be found between the necessary design expenditure and the amount of circuitry required.

1.1.3 Pseudo-duplication

Minero *et al.* (1972) describe the method of pseudo-duplication for error detection in the case of combinational functions, especially of arithmetic and binary logical functions. The data are processed twice in succession by the same circuit, but along different data paths, and are checked for equality after a suitable intermediate storage operation. In this case circuit duplication is replaced, in essence, by a longer processing time. The method of pseudo-duplication may also be implemented in software, as discussed at the end of this chapter for the case of floating point addition.

Figure 1.4 shows the basic circuit for checking a binary, component-wise connection between two operands, in this case of four-digit ones, $x = x_4 x_3 x_2 x_1$ and $x' = x'_4 x'_3 x'_2 x'_1$, to $x \bigcirc x' = x_4 \bigcirc x'_4$, $x_3 \bigcirc x'_3$, $x_2 \bigcirc x'_2$, $x_1 \bigcirc x'_1$, by means of an ALU (arithmetic-logic unit). The operation $\bigcirc$ may, for instance, be a disjunction, equivalence, implication, etc.

First the switches s_1 and s_2 connect their inputs with their right-hand outputs. The values x_1, x_2, x_3, x_4 and x'_1, x'_2, x'_3, x'_4 are then applied to the inputs 1, 2, 3, 4 and 1', 2', 3', 4', respectively. The ALU sends the results $x_1 \bigcirc x'_1$, $x_2 \bigcirc x'_2$, $x_3 \bigcirc x'_3$, $x_4 \bigcirc x'_4$ to its outputs 1, 2, 3, 4 and the output data are stored in the positions 1, 2, 3, 4 of register 3.

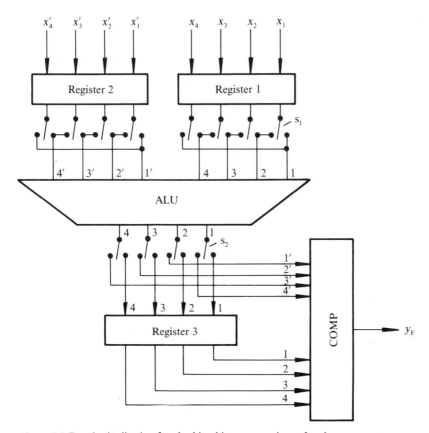

Figure 1.4 Pseudo-duplication for checking binary operations of each component.

In the next step the switches s_1 and s_2 connect their inputs with their left-hand outputs, so that the values x_1, x_2, x_3, x_4 and x'_1, x'_2, x'_3, x'_4 are applied to the ALU inputs 2, 3, 4, 1 and 2′, 3′, 4′, 1′, respectively, and the results $x_1 \bigcirc x'_1$, $x_2 \bigcirc x'_2$, $x_3 \bigcirc x'_3$, $x_4 \bigcirc x'_4$ appear at the outputs 2, 3, 4, 1 of the ALU. The left-hand ALU outputs 2, 3, 4, 1 are connected to the (comparator) inputs 1′, 2′, 3′, 4′, respectively, so that the values $x_1 \bigcirc x'_2$, $x_2 \bigcirc x'_2$, $x_3 \bigcirc x'_3$, $x_4 \bigcirc x'_4$ calculated on different data paths are recombined in the correct digit order in the comparator.

Suppose that output 3 of the ALU exhibits a stuck-at-1 error and that the operands 0110 and 0010 are subjected to a component-wise XOR operation in the ALU. If the switches s_1 and s_2 connect their inputs with their right-hand outputs, then 0100 is stored in register 3. If the switches s_1 and s_2 connect their inputs with their left-hand outputs, then first 1100 and 0100 are subjected to the XOR operation, which gives, taking into account the stuck-at-1 error, 1100, so that 0110 and 0100 are applied to the comparator and the latter indicates an error signal.

If the method of pseudo-duplication is to be used to check an addition of four-digit operands, x and x', then this can be done using an ALU with $2 \times 5 = 10$ inputs and 6 outputs. The corresponding circuitry is shown in Fig. 1.5, where additionally required data paths are emphasized by thick lines.

In general it can be immediately verified that a combinational function $f(x'_1, \ldots, x'_n, x_1, \ldots, x_n) = y_1, \ldots, y_m$ can be checked by pseudo-duplication in $(n - 1)$ digits if there exist values x_0, x'_0, y_0 such that

$$f(x'_0, x'_1, \ldots, x'_{n-1}, x_0, x_1, \ldots, x_{n-1}) = y_0, y_1, \ldots, y_{m-1}$$

In more recent papers (Patel and Fung, 1982, 1983; Laha and Patel, 1983) the principle of pseudo-duplication is discussed for error detection in adders, multipliers and dividers, and in Cheng and Patel (1984) it is applied to error detection in an iterative linear array.

In processors handling different data sizes it is possible to use duplication and pseudo-duplication in a mixed manner. Thus in Wing and Glen (1982) a processor is considered that has to process data of word size and addresses of double word size. The structure of the processing unit is designed for double word sized data. Data are processed simultaneously in the two halves of the processor and the results are compared (duplication), whereas addresses are calculated twice in succession. The first result is temporarily stored. The operation is repeated with interchanged values (pseudo-duplication).

We will now explain how the method of pseudo-duplication may be applied for checking the operation of floating point addition according to Hahn and Gössel (1991). In this case the method was implemented by software. A floating point number Z is represented by

$$Z = (\text{sign } Z, \exp Z, 0.f(Z) = 0.z_n \cdots z_1 z_0)$$

where sign $Z \in \{0, 1\}$ is the sign of Z, $\exp Z$ is an integer (in ones complement

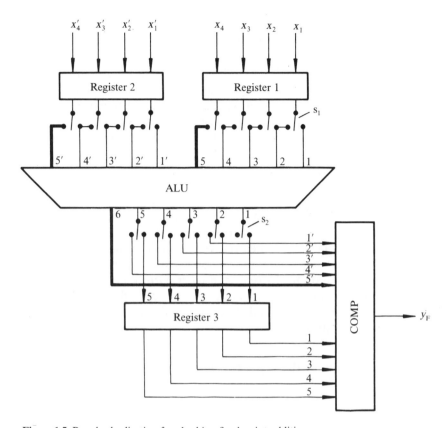

Figure 1.5 Pseudo-duplication for checking fixed point addition.

representation, generally also biased) and $0 \cdot f(Z)$, with $0.5 \leqslant f(Z) < 1$, $z_n = 1$ for $Z \neq 0$, is the mantissa. Z can be expressed as

$$Z = -1^{\text{sign } z} * 0.f(Z) * 2^{(\exp z - \text{bias})}$$

The binary values $z_n, \ldots, z_0$ are called the components of the mantissa here. We suppose that the reader is familiar with the basic principles of floating point addition, consisting of the steps of comparison of operands, alignment, addition, normalization, rounding, post-normalization. For details see, for example, Cavanagh (1984) and Kulisch (1976). For simplicity of presentation we restrict ourselves to the addition of floating point numbers with equal signs.

To derive an appropriate identity for checking floating point additions we rely on the fact that we have

$$Z = (\text{sign } Z, \exp Z, 0.z_n \cdots z_1 z_0)$$

$$D(Z) = (\text{sign } Z, \exp Z + 1.0.10 \cdots 0)$$

$$(D(Z) + Z) = (\text{sign } Z, (\exp Z) + 1, 0.z_n \cdots z_1 z_0)$$

After summing Z and $D(Z)$, the components $z_n, \ldots, z_0$ of the mantissa $0.f(Z)$ are shifted one bit position to the right and a 1 is added into the leading bit position of the mantissa. The exponent is incremented by 1.

The influence of a restricted word length of a floating point processor and the different possible rounding modes are considered in detail in Hahn and Gössel (1991). Let $X = (\text{sign } X, \exp X = a, 0.f(X))$ and $Y = (\text{sign } Y, \exp Y = b, 0.f(Y))$ be floating point numbers with sign $X = \text{sign } Y, |X| \geqslant |Y|$ and let $D(X) = (\text{sign } X, a + 1, 0.10 \cdots 0)$. Then the floating point addition will be monitored by checking

$$((X + Y) + D(X)) = [X + D(X)] + Y$$

In this equation, different data paths are used on the left and right sides to add the components of $f(X)$ and $f(Y)$, respectively. To compute $X + Y$, the components of $f(X)$ and $f(Y)$, after proper alignment, are added in their normal positions and then shifted one bit position to the right by adding $D(X)$. To compute $X + D(X)$, the components of the mantissa $f(X)$ are shifted one bit position to the right and, after correct alignment of Y with respect to $X + D(X)$, the components of $f(Y)$ are added to the shifted components of $f(X)$. This method of pseudo-duplication could be completely implemented by software.

1.1.4 Regeneration of the Input Symbols

For a combinational or sequential circuit S which has an inverse circuit S^{-1}, so that the series connection of S and S^{-1} implements identical mapping, errors of the circuits S or S^{-1} can be detected in a simple manner by regenerating the input symbols of S (cf. Fig. 1.6). The original input of S and the input $\tilde{x}$ regenerated from the output y by S^{-1} are then compared

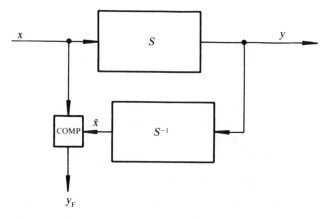

Figure 1.6 Regeneration of input symbols.

with each other. If $x \neq \tilde{x}$, then there is a failure in S, in S^{-1} or in both circuits (Sellers *et al.*, 1968).

At first one would hope to find cases where implementation of the inverse circuits would require less expenditure than that of the original one. However, it is generally known that every error detection circuit, which has no reference to a specific error model and hence also an error detection circuit barrel on the regeneration of the input symbols, has at least as many non-equivalent states on the circuit to be monitored (cf. page 154). The number of states is only a rough estimation of the implementation costs of a circuit and it may be that the combinational blocks of the inverse circuit are simpler than the corresponding combinational blocks of the original circuit. In any case it is easier to detect design errors by the method of regeneration of input symbols than by duplication and comparison.

For combinational circuits having several inputs and several outputs the required overheads can be reduced by regenerating the input symbols only for some of the inputs, accepting that only part of the errors will then be detected. If only the input symbols of a subset of the inputs are regenerated, then the existence of the inverse circuit will be required for only these inputs.

Figure 1.7 shows the basic design of the circuit for the case where only the input symbols $x_i, \ldots, x_{i+k}$ are regenerated from among the input symbols

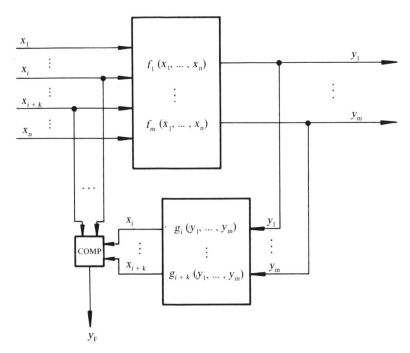

Figure 1.7 Regeneration of a subset of input symbols.

Table 1.2

x_1	x_2	$f_1(x_1, x_2) = y_1$	$f_2(x_1, x_2) = y_2$
0	0	0	0
0	1	0	0
1	0	0	1
1	1	1	0

$x_1, \ldots, x_n$. Here an input symbol x_i, $x_i \in \{0, 1\}$, is regenerable if there exists a Boolean function $g_i \colon Y^m \to X$ such that

$$g_i(f_1(x_1, \ldots, x_n), \ldots, f_m(x_1, \ldots, x_n)) = x_i$$

Obviously this is the case if, for all values $x_1^0, \ldots, x_n^0$ and $\tilde{x}_1^0, \ldots, \tilde{x}_n^0$ with $x_i^0 \neq \tilde{x}_i^0$, there exists a $j \in \{1, \ldots, m\}$ such that

$$f_j(x_1^0, \ldots, x_n^0) \neq f_j(\tilde{x}_1^0, \ldots, \tilde{x}_n^0)$$

which is easy to check from a table of values for the functions $f_1, \ldots, f_n$. The function g_i, provided it exists, is partially determined by this table.

To illustrate this using a simple example, let us consider a combinational circuit with two inputs and two outputs, which implements the functions

$$y_1 = f_1(x_1, x_2) = x_1 \wedge x_2$$

$$y_2 = f_2(x_1, x_2) = x_1 \wedge \bar{x}_2$$

The table of values for the functions f_1 and f_2 is shown in Table 1.2.

Different values of x_1 are assigned different values of y_1 and y_2 in Table 1.2, so x_1 is regenerable. On the other hand, the values $x_2 = 0$ as well as $x_2 = 1$ are assigned $y_1 y_2 = 00$, so x_2 is not regenerable.

For $g_1(y_1, y_2)$ it is seen from Table 1.2 that $g_1(0, 0) = 0$, $g_1(1, 0) = g_1(0, 1) = 1$, while $g_1(1, 1)$ remains indeterminate, so g_1 can, for instance, be chosen to be $g_1(y_1, y_2) = y_1 \vee y_2$. If the circuit considered outputs 01 or 11 instead of 10, or else 10 or 11 instead of 01, such an error will not be detected.

For sequential circuits with several inputs and several outputs, to our knowledge there have not been any systematic investigations on the regeneration of the input symbols for a subset of the inputs. Some results for sequential circuits, especially showing how to modify originally non-invertible automata into invertible ones, for which the input signals can then be regenerated, are presented in Betrand *et al.* (1974).

1.1.5 Special Examples of Duplication and Comparison

At the end of this section, we mention some special examples of duplication and comparison. In the first examples the redundance that exists in the normal circuit is also used for monitoring the behaviour.

It is well known that systolic arrays are mostly partially utilized at any time for computations. In Hellwagner (1986) the error detection in systolic arrays is investigated. At any time during processing these arrays are used only partially for calculation. The unused cells of the array duplicate the functions of each of the used neighbouring cells, producing results in duplicate. Neighbours are then compared. There is little extra expenditure for hardware and time required in order to achieve this.

In Berdard and Jaswa (1987), in a clock generating system designed with triple redundancy, the available redundancy is used in a simple way for error detection. The output of the majority element is compared with the output of each of the clock generator circuits, which exist in triplicate. If it is assumed that at any time considered only one of the clock generator circuits or only the majority circuit is defective, then by means of the three comparison signals it is possible to detect an error in the clock generator circuit or in the majority circuit. In principle the approach described in Berdard and Jaswa (1987) can be applied to all systems with system triplication and majority selection.

Of special interest is the method described in Criswell (1985) for monitoring normalization operations as they are required in floating point operations. This involves first completing a normalization operation and then testing whether it needs to be repeated (which could mean that the normalization failed). The second part is only a test and thus requires less hardware than complete normalization, so that in total the expenditure remains less than that required for duplication and comparison. However, this method only tests for errors in the exponent.

The method described in Horwarth (1985) can also be considered as a modification of duplication and comparison. It is used to monitor the correct order of succession of the states of a finite state automation $A = (X, Z, f)$, where X and Z are the input and state sets, respectively, and $f: Z \times X \to Z$ is the state transition function.

By means of a combinational circuit, K_1 (called an encoder in Horwarth, 1985), every state $z \in Z$ is assigned an n-digit number $K_1(z)$, preferable in l-out-of-m code. A second combinational circuit, K_2, also assigns to every pair (z, x), $z \in Z$, $x \in X$, an n-ary binary number $K_2(z, x)$ such that

$$z(t) = f(z(t-1), x(t-1)) \text{ implies } K_1(z(t)) = K_2(z(t-1), x(t-1))$$

$K_1(z(t))$ and $K_2(z(t-1), x(t-1))$ are compared by the use of a comparator COMP. If they are different an error will be indicated. Since $z(t)$ is available one clock cycle after $z(t-1)$, $K_2(z(t-1), x(t-1))$ has to be compared with $K_1(z(t))$ with a delay of one clock cycle. This requires a register R of word length n.

This method is illustrated in Fig. 1.8. The combinational circuit K_2 is functionally determined as a serial connection of the state transition function f of the automaton A and the combinational circuit K_1. If we have $K_1(z) = z$ for all $z \in Z$ the method is similar to duplication and comparison. Compared

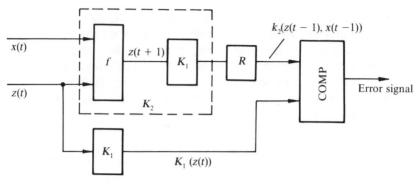

Figure 1.8 Monitoring the correct succession of states of an automaton.

with duplication and comparison, the reduced expenditure results from the fact that different states may be assigned by K_1 equal binary numbers. The desired faults are detected by considering the state diagram of the circuit in question in detail when determining K_1. However, this is not discussed in Horwarth (1985).

The adaption of this method to a given error model is considered in Chapter 3.

1.2 APPLICATION OF CODES

The applicability of error detecting codes to the monitoring of digital circuits has been extensively investigated. Historically, error detecting codes were first developed to monitor data transfer on noisy channels, and were therefore optimally adapted to the error models of independent single bit errors or of error bursts of a certain maximum length. Introductions to the coding theory of communication engineering are given, for example, in Peterson and Weldon (1972) and Swoboda (1973). A survey of the application of coding theory in the design of reliable computers is given in Fujiwara and Pradhan (1990). A very comprehensive description of almost all aspects of error control coding is contained in Rao and Fujiwara (1989).

Generally, the function of error detection coding is to add some extra bits in the binary representation of data in such a way that it is possible to detect erroneously represented data. In this section we will explain some basic notions and principles of codes and also discuss in more detail the applicability of codes for monitoring digital circuits.

Let us start with a simple example. If the symbols a, b, c and d are represented in binary form by 00, 01, 10 and 11, respectively, a one-bit-error changing, for example 00 into 01, changes the representation of a into the representation of b and it can not be detected. If we encode the symbols a, b, c, d by $C(a) = 000$, $C(b) = 011$, $C(c) = 101$, $C(d) = 110$, respectively, then an additional parity bit is appended to the original binary representations of a, b, c and d. The number of ones in each of the code words is always even, and a one-bit-error changing, for example 000 into 010, can be detected since the number of ones in the erroneous word 010 is odd.

The subset {000, 011, 101, 011} of all binary words of length 3, {000, 001, 010, 011, 100, 101, 110, 111}, is a code. This subset can be characterized by the fact that the number of ones in each of its code words is even. It is called an even parity code. Since 010 is not an element of this code it can be detected as erroneous. The subset {001, 010, 100} is also a code, a so-called 1-out-of-3 code. Exactly one bit of three bits is one. The subset {000, 001, 100} may also be considered as a code. Generally, a set of code words or a code is a subset of a given set of words.

As already mentioned, the symbols a, b, c and d of our example are coded using the even parity code to detect single-bit errors. The error detection capability of a code is to a large extent determined by the distance between its code words. As an example of a distance, the widely used Hamming distance $d_H(y_1, y_2)$ between two words $y_1 = y_{11} \cdots y_{1n}$ and $y_2 = y_{21} \cdots y_{2n}$ is defined as the number of disagreements between its corresponding components. In the binary case we have y_{1i}, $Y_{2i} \in \{0, 1\}$ for $i = 1, \ldots, n$ and the distance may be computed by

$$d_H(y_1, y_2) = \sum_{i=1}^{n} (y_{1i} \oplus y_{2i})$$

Thus for every pair y_1, $y_2 \in \{000, 011, 101, 110\}$, $y_1 \neq y_2$, the Hamming distance $d_H(y_1, y_2)$ equals 2.

The distance of a code is the smallest distance between two of its code words. The distance between every two words of the code {000, 011, 101, 110} is 2. Therefore the Hamming distance of this code is 2. If the Hamming distance of a code is d then all errors changing at most $d - 1$ bits can be detected.

As mentioned above, error-detecting codes were first developed to monitor data transfer on noisy channels. Therefore they were optimally adapted to the error models of independent single bit errors or of error bursts of a certain maximum length.

The coding methods developed in communications engineering are applicable to the monitoring of data paths and memories (exclusively for address calculation) without any essential problems (cf. Sellers et al., 1968; Wakerly, 1978). Here, especially in memory structures, error-detecting and error-correcting codes are frequently used. The last property gains importance with an increasing degree of integration of memory integrated circuits (ICs). Stochastic external disturbances, such as incident alpha particles and also variations in the quality of memory ICs, cause some errors in these structures. Codes are often chosen that allow single-bit error correction and the safe detection of two-bit errors.

Today such error detection and correction circuits based on Hamming codes are offered to the user for data sizes of 8, 16 and 32 bits on large-scale integration circuits. They are intended mainly for use in minicomputer systems (Bryce, 1984; Willmaun, 1984; Bernstein, 1985; Eglauer, 1985). A survey of error detection and correction circuits made by different manufacturers is given in Borisow (1984).

As an adaption of coding theory to error detection and correction in memories we mention here a special solution (Nagamo and Takahahi, 1983) where a specific procedure is initiated upon detection of a single-bit error. The erroneous bit is corrected and the corrected data word is then rewritten into memory. If the error occurs again when the read operation is repeated, the error is deemed to be a permanent one. For this particular case, the memory matrix contains an additional column to which the defective bit position is transferred. For the present, this makes the used memory space again free from permanent errors. A repair may then be carried out during the next system maintenance.

A proposal for utilizing the precharge time required in dynamic random access memories (RAMs) for the simultaneous correction of single-bit errors is given in Ziegler *et al.* (1983). The area/performance cost of implementing corresponding codes on-chip are of growing interest, especially for large RAM sizes. They have been investigated in, for example, Jarwala and Pradhan (1987).

In the monitoring of data paths, apart from the usual application of a certain code, there are also solutions known where combinations of different code types are used. Thus two-dimensional data arrays that are to be transferred can be encoded in both the horizontal and the vertical directions. A so-called product code adds individual check symbols to every row and every column. If the code words in the horizontal and the vertical directions are interdependent, we speak of linked codes. These are very efficient, but generally require very complex encoding and decoding circuitry.

Unlike data paths and memories, individual failures of the components in general digital circuits cause a variety of functional errors. Thus a single component failure (fault) or a transient error may cause errors in several parts of a result. This is the reason why problems arise in the application of error detection codes to error detection in random logic. Let us illustrate this fact by a simple example. Figure 1.9 shows a circuit implementing

$$y_1 = (x_1 \wedge x_2) \oplus (x_2 \vee x_3)$$

$$y_2 = x_2 \vee x_3$$

The corresponding table of values for the correct implementation and for the faults 'line 4 stuck-at-0 (4/0)', 'line 5 stuck-at-1 (5/1)', 'bridging between line 1 and 3 (brid(1, 3))', 'line 5 stuck-at-1 and simultaneously line 4 stuck-at-1' are given in Table 1.3. The bridging is modelled as a wired OR,

Table 1.3

			Correct		4/0		5/1		brid(1, 3)		5/1, 4/1	
x_1	x_2	x_3	y_1	y_2	y_1	y_2	y_1	y_2	y_1	y_2	y_1	y_2
0	0	0	0	0	0	0	1	1■	0	0	0	1◆
0	0	1	0	0	0	0	1	1■	1	1■	0	1◆
0	1	0	1	1	1	1	1	1	1	1	0	1◆
0	1	1	0	1	1	1◆	0	1	0	1	0	1
1	0	0	1	1	1	1	1	1	1	1	0	1◆
1	0	1	1	1	1	1	1	1	1	1	0	1◆
1	1	0	1	1	1	1	1	1	0	1◆	0	1◆
1	1	1	0	1	1	1◆	0	1	0	1	0	1

i.e. in case of bridging between line 1 and line 3 the circuit of Fig. 1.9 implements

$$y_1 = ((x_1 \vee x_3) \wedge x_2) \oplus (x_1 \vee x_2 \vee x_3)$$

$$y_2 = x_1 \vee x_2 \vee x_3$$

In the case of a single stuck-at-0 fault of line 4 two one-bit errors, marked by ◆ in Table 1.3, may occur. However, in the case of a single stuck-at-1 fault of line 5 two two-bit errors, marked by ■, are generated. No one-bit error is possible for this fault. The bridging between line 1 and line 3 may result in a two-bit error marked by ■ and a one-bit error marked by ◆. If, simultaneously, the single faults 'line 5 stuck-at-1' and 'line 4 stuck-at-1' are present then only one-bit errors may occur in the circuit of Fig. 1.9.

This simple example shows that in general there is no correspondence between the number of technical faults and the number of erroneous bits of the considered circuit. This is the main reason that one has to be careful in applying error detection codes for fault detection in (random) combinational and sequential circuits. The application of codes may be reasonable for some special circuits, especially for circuits with a large degree of regularity, e.g. for decoders, adders, multipliers or for circuits designed in a special way.

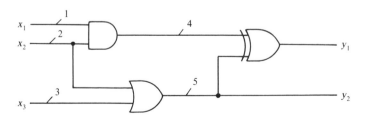

Figure 1.9 Special combinational circuit.

In some cases it is possible to assign a weight to a functional error 'y erroneous in y''. Here the weight is understood to be the number of technical faults required to produce this functional error, and it depends on the fault model considered and especially upon which faults have to be regarded as single ones. If it is possible to determine a code for which the distance between the code of the correct value y and the code of the erroneous value y' is close or equal to the weight 'y erroneous in y'' then it is reasonable to apply error detecting codes for monitoring technical faults of the considered circuit.

If single failures only influence one part of the result, then the parity check codes using the Hamming distance between binary vectors are reasonable. This is always the case if the different parts of a circuit are implemented by independent gates.

For circuits divided into independent slices of a width of b bits each, so-called b-adjacent codes, parity check codes over $GF(2^b)$ are reasonable (Bossen, 1970; Wakerly, 1978). A generalization, a so-called (b, k)-adjacent code, is described in Arlat and Carter (1984). For adders where single failures in the circuit may affect the full word size of the result, codes with a modular arithmetic weight are used. Codes are also extensively used for the design of fault tolerant sequential circuits. The states of the considered automaton are coded as elements of an appropriate code space (cf., for example, Reed and Chiang, 1970; Larsen and Reed, 1972).

The application of error detection codes for monitoring adders is described in Sec. 1.2.3. In this case the regular structure of adders and their simple functional description allow the application of special arithmetic codes.

A much more difficult problem is to be solved for asynchronous automata. The distance between all of the intermediate states of different state transitions must be larger than $2m + 1$ if m faults can be tolerated (cf. Pradhan and Reddy, 1973).

After these introductory remarks, we shall now give several examples of the application of different codes to error detection in digital circuits.

1.2.1 Parity Checking

For a combinational circuit f_C with n inputs and m outputs the principle of parity checking is illustrated in Fig. 1.10. The circuit f_C implements the function $f = (f^1, \ldots, f^m)$, with

$$y_i = f^i(x_1, \ldots, x_n), \qquad i = 1, \ldots, m$$

where

$$f^i: \{0, 1\}^n \to \{0, 1\} \text{ are } n\text{-ary Boolean functions}$$

The so-called parity prediction function f_P is determined by

$$f_P(x_1, \ldots, x_n) = f^1(x_1, \ldots, x_n) \oplus \cdots \oplus f^m(x_1, \ldots, x_n)$$

The outputs $y_1, \ldots, y_m$ of f_C are added modulo 2 and compared with the

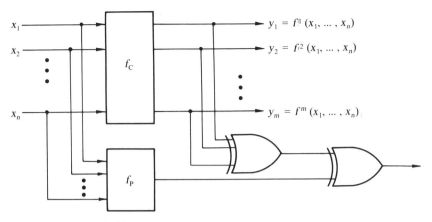

Figure 1.10 Parity checking.

predicted by f_P parity. If the predicted parity and the parity computed as the modulo-2 sum of the outputs of f_C disagree, an error is indicated.

The general method of parity prediction now will be applied to the circuit of Fig. 1.9, implementing the functions

$$y_1 = (x_1 \wedge x_2) \oplus (x_2 \vee x_3)$$

$$y_2 = x_3 \vee x_2$$

In this case the parity prediction function f_P is determined by

$$f_P(x_1, x_2, x_3) = (x_1 \wedge x_2) \oplus (x_2 \vee x_3) \oplus (x_3 \vee x_2) = x_1 \wedge x_2$$

The predicted parity $f_P(x_1, x_2, x_3) = x_1 \wedge x_2$ has to be compared with $y_1 \oplus y_2$, as shown in Fig. 1.11. The parity checking of Fig. 1.11 detects all

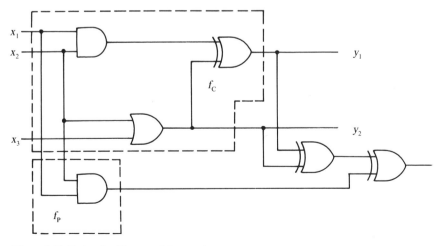

Figure 1.11 Parity checking, special example.

errors due to fault 4/0, no error due to fault 5/1, one error of the possible two errors caused by the bridging fault brid$(1, 3)$ and all errors caused by the double fault 4/1 and 5/1.

Parity checking is well adapted to detecting single-bit errors but not to the detection of technical faults. However, because of its conceptual simplicity it is widely used in computers. As a general method it is first described in detail in Davis and Harris (1971). Often only the data paths are checked by parity bits. After the processing of data by an adder the parity bit is newly generated. The adder is not monitored or in some cases is monitored by other means.

We now refer to an interesting modification of parity prediction (Parchomenko and Sogomonyan, 1981; Fujiwara, 1983). A combinational circuit with n inputs $x_1, \ldots, x_n$ and m outputs $y_1, \ldots, y_m$ implementing the Boolean functions $F_i(x_1, \ldots, x_n)$, $i = 1, \ldots, m$, is to be monitored. The outputs are first subdivided into disjoint groups Y_j, $j = 0, \ldots, r - 1$; $r \geqslant 2$, $Y_j = y_1^j, \ldots, y_{mj}^j$, and the outputs of each group are combined by the XOR operation, so that for each group Y_j a parity bit $g_j(Y_j) = y_1^j \oplus y_2^j \oplus \cdots \oplus y_{mj}^j$ is formed. The relation

$$f_j(x_1, \ldots, x_n) = h(x_1, \ldots, x_n) \oplus g_j(Y_j), \qquad j = 1, \ldots, r - 1 \qquad (1.1)$$

defines the functions f_j, where, in the present case, $h(x_1, \ldots, x_n)$ is an arbitrary Boolean function of n arguments used in the optimization of the error detection circuit.

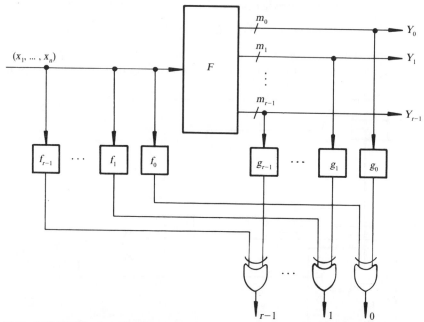

Figure 1.12 Modification of parity prediction.

The basic design of the error detection circuit is shown in Fig. 1.12. From Eq. (1.1), for all j, $j = 0, \ldots, r - 1$, one has

$$f_j(x_1, \ldots, x_n) \oplus g_j(Y_j) = h(x_1, \ldots, x_n) \tag{1.2}$$

and in the case of correct operation of both the original and the error detection circuit the latter applies the signals $0 \cdots 0$ or $1 \cdots 1$ to the outputs $0, 1, \ldots, r - 1$. A different output indicates an error. Determination of the function h and the subdivision of the outputs into groups is then investigated in detail.

For sequential circuits the parity bit check can reasonably be used for state monitoring whenever the parity of the successor state can be determined from that of the present state. In Fulton (1971) the parity bit check is described for shift registers and counters. Figure 1.13 shows the error detection circuit using parity bit checking for a four-stage shift register with the feedback logic f_1 (cf., for example, Gössel, 1972). The parity

$$P(z(t)) = z_1(t) \oplus z_2(t) \oplus z_3(t) \oplus z_4(t)$$

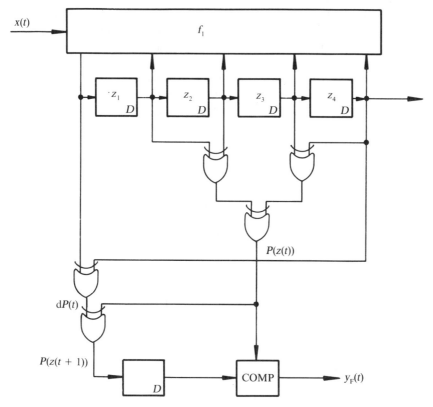

Figure 1.13 Parity checking for a shift register.

of the state vector of the register at time t is determined in an XOR tree. The parity variation

$$dP(t) = z_4(t) \oplus f_1(x(t), z_1(t), z_2(t), z_3(t), z_4(t))$$

is formed by connecting the output of the shift register through EXCLUSIVE-OR circuits to the input of the first delay flip-flop. $P(z(t))$ is compared with $P(z(t-1)) \oplus dP(t-1)$ in the comparator COMP. A single-bit error in the state transfer of the shift register then causes a difference between $P(z(t))$ and $P(z(t-1)) + dP(-1)$ to occur.

Similarly, it is also possible to monitor the state of a counter by parity bit checking (cf. also Taylor, 1984). In the case of the Gray-code counter the check reduces to checking whether the parity changes for each input 1.

In Hsiao et al. (1977) an autonomous linear shift register is introduced for which all the states of a cycle are code words of an (n, k)-cyclic code. The characteristic polynom $\Phi(x)$ of the autonomous linear shift register is of the form

$$\Phi(x) = g(x) \cdot p(x)$$

where $g(x)$ is a generator polynom of an (n, k)-cyclic code and $p(x)$ is a primitive polynom of degree k. If the code was a minimum-distance d code, then all the faults that produce $d - 1$ errors in the states are detectable when checking the code structure.

Checking an interface by a modified parity bit circuit is described in (Jackowski and Moyer, 1985). The lines are checked in the control mode, i.e. when there is no data transfer. The control lines are checked by a common parity bit circuit. All inputs of the data lines are connected to the same control line in the control mode. At the outputs of the data lines connected in this way a simple combinational circuit is used to derive an error signal, which then indicates an error if at least one of the data lines is open; the corresponding control line carries a control signal.

In Procter (1985) the clock signal is included in the parity check. First a modulo-2 counter is used to derive a periodic signal from the clock signal. This has double the period and is connected to the error signals of the individual checked subcircuits by an EXCLUSIVE-OR circuit.

If the error signal of the subcircuits is determined by parity bit checking, then the periodic signal provides another bit for parity bit checking. If there is no error either in the circuit or in the clock generation, then the error detection circuit of each subcircuit outputs a 0 at each even time and a 1 at each odd time. This condition is checked by another simple circuit.

1.2.2 Error Detection in Decoders

Various interesting error detection circuits are known for decoders with n inputs and 2^n outputs, by which an n-digit binary number is assigned a

Table 1.4

y_0	y_1	y_2	y_3	F_1	F_2	F_3	F_4
0	0	0	0	1	1	1	1
1	0	0	0	0	0	0	0
0	1	0	0	0	0	0	0
0	0	1	0	0	0	0	0
0	0	0	1	0	0	0	0
1	1	0	0	1	0	1	0
1	0	1	0	1	1	1	0
1	0	0	1	1	1	0	0
0	1	1	0	1	1	0	0
0	1	0	1	1	1	1	0
0	0	1	1	1	0	1	0
1	1	1	0	1	1	1	0
1	1	0	1	1	1	1	0
1	0	1	1	1	1	1	0
0	1	1	1	1	1	1	0
1	1	1	1	1	1	1	0

2^n-digit binary number containing exactly one 1. Error detection for decoders is a good example of how it is possible to apply error detection codes in a reasonable way for a very special type of circuit investigating very special properties of these circuits and their implementation.

Since such a decoder always outputs elements of a 1-out-of-2^n code, one can first use an error detection circuit, F_{1s}, to check whether exactly 1 one and $2^n - 1$ zeros are actually output from the decoder in each clock cycle. For $n = 2$ the table of values for the corresponding Boolean function F_1 with $2^2 = 4$ arguments is shown in Table 1.4. It is to be implemented by an error detection circuit, when $y_0, \ldots, y_3$ are the outputs of the decoder.

Especially for large n, however, the technical expenditure for such a complete error detection is relatively high (cf. Sellers *et al.*, 1968). A comparatively simple and low-expenditure variant using OR and AND gates is described in Christensen (1975).

Moreover, simple error detection circuits that can readily be implemented for large n are also known for decoders. In these circuits it is accepted that not all technical failures are detected with each bit pattern where they affect the behaviour. In Sellers *et al.* (1968) it is shown how such a circuit can be adapted in a very simple way to the detection of single failures due to technological causes.

Figure 1.14 shows an error detection circuit F_{2s} with a relatively low circuit expenditure for $n = 2$. In each case 2^{n-1} out of the 2^n outputs of the decoder are connected by an OR operation, and the outputs of the OR gates are compared for equality. Figure 1.14 shows the first two outputs, y_0 and

y_1, and the last two outputs, y_2 and y_3, of the four outputs of the decoder. These outputs are connected through OR gates D_2 and D_3, respectively, whose outputs are fed to an EXCLUSIVE-NOR gate, which outputs the error signal. The F_{2s} error detection circuit implements the function F_2 shown in Table 1.4. In contrast to F_{1s}, the erroneous outputs 1100 and 0011 are not detected as errors by F_{2s}. On the other hand, the expenditure for error detection becomes comparatively low with increasing n.

To adapt the error detection circuit as closely as possible to the detection of single failures due to technological causes, in a further step the outputs of the decoder are subdivided in a special way into two classes of outputs connected by OR gates. For that purpose each output of the decoder is assigned a weight. Here the weight of an output A is the number of ones of the input bit pattern that causes a 1 at the output A. Thus the output y_0 has the weight 0, because the input bit pattern 00, for which $y_0 = 1$, does not contain any ones. The outputs y_1 and y_2 have the weight 1 and the output y_3 has the weight 2. The corresponding input bit patterns are 01, 10 and 11, respectively. The parity of an output is obtained from its weight. Outputs with even weight have the parity 0 while outputs with odd weight have the parity 1. The parity of y_0 and y_3 is 0; that of y_1 and y_2 is 1.

According to Hong (1972), the outputs with parity 0 must be fed to a first OR gate and those with parity 1 to a second OR gate. The outputs of the two OR gates are compared by an equivalence element. The error detection circuit just described, denoted by F_{3s}, implements the function F_3 shown in Table 1.4. The two erroneous output bit patterns 1001 and 0110 are not detected as errors by F_3.

Although the number of erroneous bit patterns not detected as errors is equal for F_{2s} and F_{3s}, it is preferable to use the circuit F_{3s} if the following single failures are assumed to be possible:

1. Stuck-at-0 failure for arbitrary points.
2. Stuck-at-1 failure for arbitrary points.
3. Short circuit of NOT element, which then behaves like a wire.

To illustrate this statement, consider some examples of the failures mentioned above.

1. Stuck-at-0 failure at the output y_0, point a in Fig. 1.14. Input of 00 makes $y_0 = y_1 = y_2 = y_3 = 0$. In this case D_0 and D_1 of F_{3s} as well as D_2 and D_3 of F_{2s} output the value 0, so that the failure is detected in both circuits. For other bit patterns, this failure has no functional effect and therefore cannot be detected.
2. Stuck-at-1 failure at the output of a NOT element, point b in Fig. 1.14. Input of 11 makes $y_0 = y_1 = 0$, $y_2 = y_3 = 1$. D_0 and D_1 each output 1, D_2 outputs 0 and D_3 outputs 1, so the failure is detected by F_{3s} but not

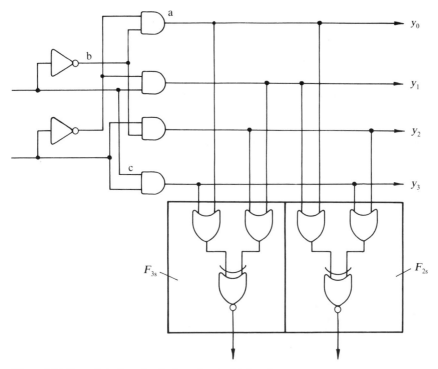

Figure 1.14 Error detection circuits for a 1-out-of-4 decoder.

by F_{2s}. Input of 10 makes $y_0 = y_1 = 1$, $Y_2 = y_3 = 0$. D_0 and D_1 again output 1, while D_2 outputs 1 and D_3 outputs 0, so the failure is detected by F_{3s} but not by F_{2s}. With other input bit patterns the failure has no effect.

3. Stuck-at-1 failure at the input of an AND element, point c in Fig. 1.14. Input of 01 makes $y_2 = y_3 = 1$, $y_0 = y_1 = 0$, so the failure is again detected by F_{3s} but not by F_{2s}. With other input bit patterns the failure has no effect.

4. Stuck-at-1 failure at the output y_0, point a in Fig. 1.14. The F_{3s} circuit detects this failure with bit patterns of 10 and 01 but not with the bit pattern 11, whereas the F_{2s} circuit detects this failure with the bit patterns 01 and 11 but not with 10. The number of bit patterns for which the failure is detected is equal for both circuits. For the bit pattern 00 the failure has no effect.

Taken altogether it turns out that the F_{3s} error detection circuit detects the single failures due to technological causes better than F_{2s}, although the expenditure for hardware is equal for both circuits. An interesting error detection circuit for a 1-out-of-n code is suggested in Powell (1973). The error detection circuit is made up of adder bit slices, and detects all n-digit binary words containing more than one 1 as erroneous.

Let us illustrate the principle using a 1-out-of-9 code as an example. The binary word $K = k_0, \ldots, k_8$ is to be checked for whether it contains a 1 in more than one bit position (cf. Fig. 1.15). Let the operand bits of the adder bit slices be denoted by A and B, and the incoming carry by c_- and the outgoing carry by c_+, respectively. The following properties can be used with advantage in the construction of the error detection circuit: the outgoing carry of an adder bit slice is 1 iff a 1 is applied to more than one of its input lines. The sum bit is 1 if a 1 is applied to either one or all three of its input lines. The error detection circuit for the 1-out-of-9 code consists of a first level of three adder bit slices, where the binary digits k_i, $i = 0, \ldots, 8$, are connected to the inputs in the way shown in Fig. 1.15. If one of the three carry-outs is 1, then an error has occurred. If more than one sum bit is 1, this also indicates an error. This condition is checked in another adder bit

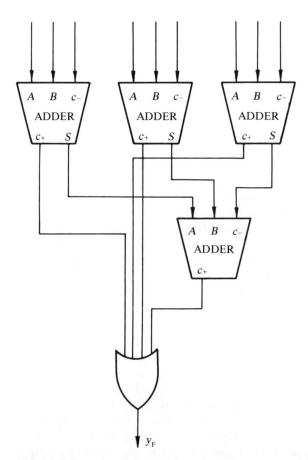

Figure 1.15 Error detection circuit for a 1-out-of-9 decoder designed by 1-bit adders.

slice; the sum bits of the adder bit slices of the first level are supplied to the three inputs. If this adder bit slice supplies a 1 to its carry output, then more than one sum bit of the first level are 1. All four carry-outs are combined by an OR element to give an error signal y_F.

In Jessep (1971) the implementation of a decoder made up of two different types of NOR gates, i.e. of NOR-a and NOR-b gates, is described. The NOR-a gates are redundantly designed so that every single electrical failure of these gates causes a stuck-at-0 error of their outputs. On the other hand, the NOR-b gates are so designed that every electrical failure causes a stuck-at-1 failure of their outputs. By means of the redundancy introduced at the signal level, only a greatly restricted set of errors is possible at the logic level, which can be detected using a very simple error detection circuit.

Figure 1.16 shows the corresponding decoder for $n = 2$. It is immediately verified that the only erroneous output possible is 0000. Here the error detection circuit consists of only one NOR-b gate with four inputs, which implements the function F_4 of Table 1.4. Since this NOR element is of the NOR-b type, every single failure of the error detection circuit is also detected.

A variant of a self-checking decoder where the input data are secured by a parity bit is described in Zola (1974). The design of a code checker for

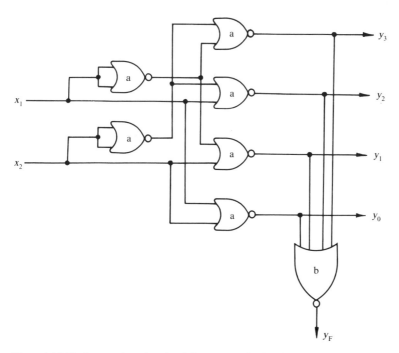

Figure 1.16 Single error detection circuit for a 1-out-of-4 decoder designed with redundant gates.

an m-out-of-n code, which is made up of threshold elements, is presented in Baugh and Wooley (1975). Further references on the monitoring of m-out-of-n codes are given in Sec. 1.2.4.

1.2.3 Checking of Adders by Modular Arithmetic Codes

An important task of computers is to perform arithmetic operations, especially the addition of two numbers. The basic approach to monitoring the addition operation by arithmetic codes will now be briefly presented. For a detailed description refer to Rao (1974).

We confine ourselves to n-digit binary numbers, $n > 0$, where n is fixed by the word length of the adder. Binary numbers are represented either in twos complement or in ones complement form. In a twos complement addition, the carry from the most significant bit is ignored. In ones complement, the carry from the most significant bit is fed back to the least significant adder stage, so that an n-digit adder performs an addition either modulo 2^n or modulo 2^{n-1}.

The aim of error detection is to detect very frequent errors, for instance errors occurring in an adder stage or in a flip-flop. If we take the Hamming weight or the Hamming metric as the basis of our considerations, then errors concerning only one or a few bits of the adder may lead to a wrong result, with a great Hamming distance forming the correct result. Thus, for example, the result 0111111 may be falsified into 1000001 by an erroneous carry of the first adder stage. The Hamming distance between the correct result and the falsified one is 6 in this case, although only a single bit was wrong in the calculation process. This shows that the Hamming distance is unsuitable for error detection in adders.

To enable error-detecting codes to be reasonably applied to adders, one uses the concept of the modular arithmetic weight of an error. The actual applied output $y' = y'_{n-1}y'_{n-2} \cdots y'_0$ of the adder under consideration may differ from the desired correct output $y = y_{n-1}y_{n-2} \cdots y_0$. The error word e is defined as

$$e = y' - y = (e_{n-1}e_{n-2} \cdots e_0)$$

where

$$e_i = y'_i - y_i, \qquad e_i \in \{0, 1, -1 = \bar{1}\}$$

The arithmetic value assigned to the error word e is

$$E = \sum_{i=0}^{n-1} e_i 2^i$$

For $y' = 101101$, $y = 011011$ one has $e = 1\bar{1}01\bar{1}0$, and hence $E = 32 - 16 + 4 - 2 = 18$.

The arithmetic weight $W(N)$ of the number N to the base 2 is defined as the minimum number of summands of the representation

$$N = a_1 \cdot 2^{j_1} + a_2 \cdot 2^{j_2} + \cdots, \qquad a_i \in \{1, -1\}$$

By way of example, $W(31) = 2$, since 31 can be represented as $2^5 - 1 = 10000\bar{1}$. Algorithmically, the arithmetic weight of a number N can be determined by representing N as a non-adjacent modified binary number. Then the number of non-zero coefficients of this representation is the arithmetic weight of N (cf. Reitwieser, 1960; Dadajev, 1981).

The modular arithmetic weight $W_m(N)$ of a number N, $0 \leqslant N < m$, is defined as

$$W_m(N) = \min(W(N), W(m - N))$$

It has the important property that for $m = 2^n$ and $m = 2^n - 1$ it is possible to define a distance $D(N, N') = W_m(N - N')$ between the numbers N and N', which in fact satisfies the triangle inequality.

For error detection in adders it is possible to use so-called AN codes, where a given number N is encoded as $A \cdot N$, with $A = $ constant. In the addition of two numbers N_1 and N_2 in an adder, the following relation holds for the sum S if an error occurs:

$$S = (A \cdot N_1 + A \cdot N_2 + E) \bmod m = (A(N_1 + N_2) \bmod m + E) \bmod m$$

If A is a divisor of m, then we obtain

$$(S) \bmod A \neq (E) \bmod A$$

If we now choose A such that, for all errors E up to a modular arithmetic weight d, we always have $(E) \bmod A \neq 0$ and that A is a divisor of m, then all errors up to a modular arithmetic weight d are detected by

$$(S) \bmod A \neq 0$$

For modifications and special versions, refer to Rao (1974).

What is problematic here is the fact that the number of possible factors is very limited and that the resulting factors are not always as easy to implement as $A = 2^k - 1$, $k > 0$. Error detection circuits of this type require a relatively high expenditure. They are not optimally adapted to the failures that actually occur due to technological causes. A modification is possible in effect only by reducing the modular arithmetic weight of the errors to be detected.

1.2.4 Self-Checking Circuits

A self-checking circuit is a circuit that indicates its own faults during normal operation from a specific class of faults. In the theory developed for self-checking circuits, inputs of self-checking circuits are supposed to be code words. If no fault occurs the input code words are mapped into output code words. A non-code output may result from a fault within the circuit or from an erroneous input.

For a more detailed description of the concept of self-checking circuits the following notions are introduced:

1. *Self-testing.* A circuit is said to be self-testing with respect to a set F of faults if for every fault in F there is at least one input code such that the corresponding output of the circuit is not a code word.
2. *Fault secure.* A circuit is said to be fault secure with respect to a set F of faults if for every fault in F there is no input code that causes the faulty circuit to output an incorrect code word. A fault secure circuit, when affected by a fault in F, outputs either the correct code word or a non-code word when a code is input.
3. *Totally self-checking.* A circuit is totally self-checking if it is self-testing and fault secure.
4. *Code disjoint.* A circuit is code disjoint if it maps all non-code words into non-code words.

If one checks the outputs of a totally self-checking combinational circuit for whether they are code words of the code considered, then all faults of the fault model F for which the circuit is self-checking are detected in the normal operation of the circuit, provided the checker does not exhibit a fault or is a totally self-checking code-disjoint code checker. This is the reason why the design of totally self-checking code checkers is of special interest. An overview of self-checking circuits is contained, for example, in Rao and Fujiwara (1989) and in Sogomonyan and Slabakov (1989).

We will first discuss a simple example of a totally self-checking code checker for binary data which are secured by a single parity bit, as described in Carter *et al.* (1971). The code words consisting of the data bits $x_1, \ldots, x_{n-1}$ and the parity bit x_n have an odd parity. The errors are implicitly assumed to be single errors. The error detection circuit consists of two separate trees of EXCLUSIVE-OR elements connecting, say, the bits $x_1, \ldots, x_m$ and $x_{m+1}, \ldots, x_n$ to $x_1 \oplus \cdots \oplus x_m$ and $x_{m+1} \oplus \cdots \oplus x_n$, where $m \geqslant 1$. For $n = 6$ and $m = 2$, Fig. 1.17 shows the error detection circuit consisting of the two EXCLUSIVE-OR trees. Owing to the odd parity of $x_1, \ldots, x_n$, the bits $x_1, \ldots, x_m$ and $x_{m+1}, \ldots, x_n$ have different parities and the error detection circuit maps n-digit code words of odd parity into 10 or 01, i.e. into a 1-out-of-2 code.

Non-code words, i.e. words of even parity, are assigned 11 or 00, i.e. non-code words. Thus the circuit is code disjoint. It is also fault secure, because any single error is localized in one of the two EXCLUSIVE-OR trees, and can falsify at most one of the two outputs of the error detection

x_1 x_2 x_3 x_4 x_5 x_6

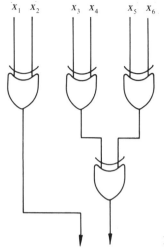

Figure 1.17 Totally self-checking code checker.

circuit. Any falsification of an output of the error detection circuit will, however, falsify a code word into one of the non-code words.

Furthermore, it can easily be seen that for every single gate fault there is an input bit pattern for which the fault affects the output of the tree in which it occurred, so that the circuit is also self-testing. There have been many papers published that deal especially with designing totally self-checking n-out-of-m code checkers. For some examples, refer to Anderson and Metze (1973), Efstathiou and Halatsis (1983), Nauya and Toma (1983), Piestra (1983) and Derbunowitsch and Neshwejew (1986).

The faults of the circuits are detected if the inputs required for detection are actually applied during normal operation. If this is not the case, then for unidirectional faults Niraj and Abraham (1984) describe how to design suitable codings for a totally self-checking code checker. The great variety of solutions, which frequently differ only in small details, will not be surveyed here.

A second very important class of self-checking circuits is the class of self-checking comparators. We will discuss two different types of self-checking comparators in more detail. Very often computational results are compared for equality and many self-checking circuits are designed using self-checking comparators. As an example, in the field of error detection circuits the method of duplication and comparison was discussed in Sec. 1.1. By this method every error of one of the duplicated systems can be detected. However, until now nothing has been said about the detection of faults within the comparator. If the comparator is self-checking, the faults of the comparator are indicated by itself and the whole circuit is a self-checking one.

A self-checking comparator with four inputs according to Carter and

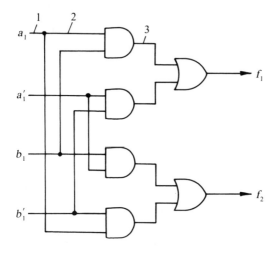

Figure 1.18 Self-checking comparator according to Carter and Schneider (1968).

Schneider (1968) is shown in Fig. 1.18. This comparator detects all of its single stuck-at-0/1 faults during normal operation if all of its correct inputs 0101, 0110, 1001 and 1010 actually occur during normal operation. This comparator compares a_1, a_2 with a'_1, a'_2 and it outputs f_1, f_2 with $f_1 = \bar{f}_2$ if and only if $a_1 = \bar{a}'_1$ and $a_2 = \bar{a}'_2$. The self-checking comparator maps the code words $(a_1 a'_1 a_2 a'_2) \in \{0101, 0110, 1001, 1010\}$ into the code words $(f_1 f_2) \in \{01, 10\}$.

The table of values for this self-checking comparator COMP is represented in Table 1.5. This comparator is self-testing with respect to all of its single stuck-at-0/1 faults.

For every single stuck-at-0/1 fault there exists a correct input (a code word) which will be mapped into a non-correct output (a non-code word) if the considered stuck-at fault occurs. This will now be illustrated for some of the stuck at 0/1 faults.

Let line 1 be stuck-at-1. Then the code input $a_1 = 0$, $a'_1 = 1$, $a_2 = 0$, $a'_2 = 1$ results in a non-code output 11 indicating a fault. If line 2 is stuck-at-1 the input 0110 gives rise to a non-code output 11 and if line 3 is stuck-at-0 then the input 1010 results in a non-code output 00. The other single stuck-at-0/1 faults can be treated in a similar way.

The comparator is also fault secure with respect to single stuck-at-0/1 faults. All the gates of the comparator influence one output only. Therefore faults concerning one gate only can change at most one output. Such a fault cannot change a correct output $f_1 f_2$ with $f_1 = \bar{f}_2$ into another correct output $f'_1 f'_2$ with $f'_1 = \bar{f}'_2$ and $f_1 \neq f'_1$.

The stuck-at faults of a direct input line may functionally change one of the inputs to its opposite value. If this is the case an input code word is

Table 1.5

a_1	a'_1	a_2	a'_2	f_1	f_2
0	0	0	0	0	0
0	0	0	1	0	0
0	0	1	0	0	0
0	0	1	1	0	0
0	1	0	0	0	0
0	1	0	1	1	0
0	1	1	0	1	0
1	0	0	0	0	0
1	0	0	0	0	0
1	0	0	1	0	1
1	0	1	0	1	0
1	0	1	1	1	1
1	1	0	0	0	0
1	1	0	1	1	1
1	1	1	0	1	1
1	1	1	1	1	1

changed into an input non-code word. Table 1.5 shows that in such a case an erroneous output always occurs, and this comparator is an example of a totally self-checking circuit. All the faults considered are detected if all the possible correct input combinations of the checker occur. If the checker is a part of a larger circuit this can not always be guaranteed.

Let us assume that only the correct inputs 1010 and 0101 can be applied to the inputs of the comparator of Fig. 1.18. Then a stuck-at-1 fault of line 2 can not be detected during normal operation. With this undetected stuck-at-1 fault the non-code input 0010 will be mapped into the code word 10 and can not be detected as erroneous.

Self-checking comparators with more than four inputs can be designed as trees of comparators with four inputs and two outputs, as shown for eight inputs in Fig. 1.19. If not all possible correct inputs actually occur then according to Kundu and Reddy (1990) delay elements can be included in the input lines of the comparators with four inputs. With the help of these delay elements, all possible correct input combinations for every comparator will occur, but the detection of an error may be considerably delayed.

A quite different approach for the design of a self-checking comparator according to Gössel and Sogomonyan (1993) is shown in Fig. 1.20. The comparator may be considered as an improved version of the comparator described in Sogomonyan (1981). One of the inputs of every XOR gate of the first level is connected to a periodically changing signal x_0. As long as no fault occurs and as long as the inputs $a_i = \bar{a}'_i$ for $i = 1, \ldots, n$ are correct, the outputs of all of the XOR gates of the second level are $\bar{x}_0$. x_0 periodically changes its value. All the outputs of the XOR gates of the second level are

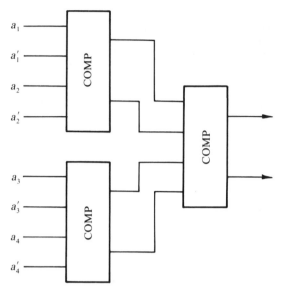

Figure 1.19 Tree of comparators.

connected to an ($\wedge$, $\vee$) gate which is controlled by x_0. This ($\wedge$, $\vee$) gate acts as an AND gate for $x_0 = 0$ and as an OR gate for $x_0 = 1$. Such controlled gates are proposed in Mercer (1980, 1986). A possible implementation of such a gate according to Mercer (1986) is shown in Fig. 1.21.

This comparator is self-testing with respect to every single fault of the XOR rates and with respect to the stuck-at-0/1 faults of the inputs and outputs of the ($\wedge$, $\vee$) gate. Depending upon the implementation of the ($\wedge$, $\vee$) gate, internal faults such as stuck-at-closed or stuck-at-open of the switches of the ($\wedge$, $\vee$) gate are also detected if this special gate is implemented in CMOS (complementary metal oxide semiconductor). The periodically changing signal x_0 must also be monitored. For a more detailed description see Gössel and Sogomonyan (1993).

In Wakerly (1974, 1978), the concepts 'self-testing' and 'fault secure' have been modified into 'partially self-testing' and 'partially fault secure' by requiring the previously mentioned properties of the circuit to be restricted to generally different input sets. In Nicolaides (1989), self-checking techniques and built-in self-test techniques are combined. The checkers and the functional units of the circuit under consideration are periodically tested using built-in self-test methods.

In the references Thoma *et al.* (1971), Takaoka and Ibaraki (1972), Diaz (1974), Sawin (1975), Maznew (1977), Dhawan and de Vries (1988) and Parekhij *et al.* (1991), the concept of a self-checking circuit is investigated for sequential circuits. Based on the assumption of single failures, methods of constructing such circuits are stated. The most extensive presentation of

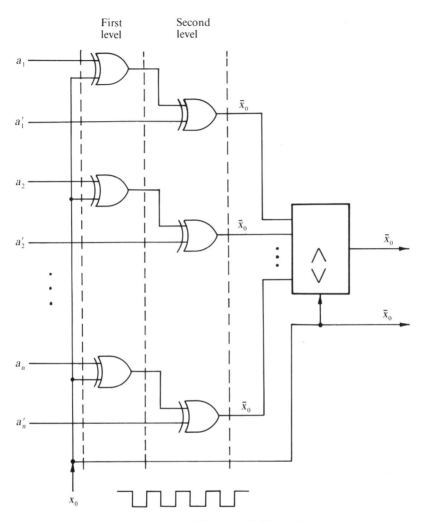

Figure 1.20 Self-checking comparator with a controlled ($\wedge$, $\vee$) gate.

this subject is given in Saposhnikov and Saposhnikov (1984). In the construction of totally self-checking sequential circuits the fact that state failures do not necessarily have an immediate effect on the output must be taken into consideration.

Following Saposhnikov and Saposhnikov (1984), we give the formulation of the problem in terms of the theory of automata. Suppose the automaton $A = (X, Y, Z, f, g)$ is to be implemented as a totally self-checking unit with the failure mode assumption of 'single stuck-at-0/1 failures or single transient errors'. To solve this problem, the implementation A_R of an automaton $\tilde{A} = (\tilde{X}, \tilde{Y}, \tilde{Z}, \tilde{f}, \tilde{g})$ with the functional error model derived from the same

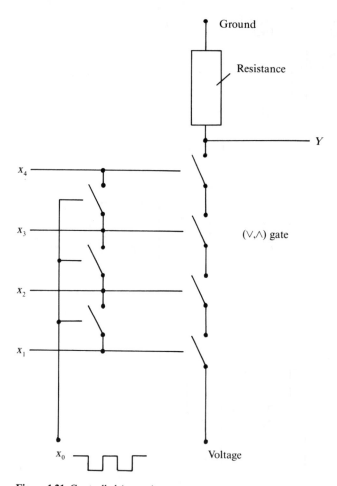

Figure 1.21 Controlled ($\wedge$, $\vee$) gate.

technological failure mode assumption of 'single stuck-at-0/1 failures or single transient errors', $F(\tilde{A}) = (\tilde{A}_0, \tilde{A}_1, \ldots, \tilde{A}_k)$ with $\tilde{A}_0 = \tilde{A}$, $\tilde{A}_i = (\tilde{X}, \tilde{Y}, Z_i, \tilde{f}_i, \tilde{g}_i)$, $Z_i \subseteq \tilde{Z}$, $i = 1, \ldots, k$, must be determined so that:

1. $\tilde{X} = X \cup X_1$ with $X_1 \cap X = \varnothing$,
   $\tilde{Y} = Y \cup Y_1$ with $Y_1 \cap Y = \varnothing$,
   $\tilde{Z} = Z \cup Z_1$ with $Z_1 \cap Z = \varnothing$.
   X_1, Y_1 and Z_1 are the erroneous input, output, and state sets respectively.
2. $\tilde{f}(z, x) = f(z, x) \in Z$, $\tilde{g}(z, x) = g(z, x)$ for all $x \in X$, $z \in Z$.
3. For all i, $1 \leqslant i \leqslant k$, there exist an $x_i \in X$ and a $z_i \in Z$ such that $f_i(z_i, x_i) \in Z_1$.
4. $f_i(z, x) = f(z, x) \in Z$ or $f_i(z, x) \in Z_1$ for all i, $1 \leqslant i \leqslant k$, and for all $x \in X$, $z \in Z$.

5. $g_i(z, x) \neq g(z, x)$ implies that $f_i(z, x) \in Z_1$ for all i, $1 \leqslant i \leqslant k$, and for all $x \in X$, $z \in Z$.
6. $f_i(z, x) \in Z_1 \cap Z_i$ for all $z \in Z_i \cap Z_1$, $x \in X$, and for all i, $1 \leqslant i \leqslant k$.
7. $\tilde{f}(z, x) \in Z_1$ for all $z \in Z_1$, $x \in X$.
8. $\tilde{f}(z, x) \in Z$, for $z \in \tilde{Z}$ and $x \in X_1$,
   $\tilde{g}(z, x) \in Y$, for $z \in \tilde{Z}$ and $x \in X_1$.

Conditions 5 and 7 are restrictive. They are due to the fact that in Saposhnikov and Saposhnikov (1984) A_R is so designed that upon the first occurrence of a single failure A reaches the state set Z_1 and remains in it. The states $z \in Z$ are encoded as elements of an n-out-of-k code. Each code word contains exactly n ones and $k - n$ zeros. The states $z \in Z_1$ are not code words. (For Moore automata, Diaz (1974) gives a somewhat less restrictive definition of a totally self-checking automaton. In particular, condition 7 is not required.)

In the design of a totally self-checking automaton, the greatest difficulty is that, where components of the automaton do not affect the correct state transfer, an accumulation of failures does not occur in these components. This could destroy the self-checking property of the automaton, by assuming an incorrect state. Taken altogether, the overhead to provide error detection is very high and cannot in practice be graduated. For details, refer to Saposhnikov and Saposhnikov (1984).

The methods of a systematic design of error detection circuits described in Chapter 2 for combinational circuits and in Chapter 3 for sequential circuits do not result in self-checking circuits. All of the assumed faults of the monitored circuit are detected if the checker is not erroneous. However, the checker is not designed as a self-checking one.

Till now, for the design of self-checking circuits only heuristic methods have been known. In most cases, self-checking circuits such as self-checking comparators are self-checking with respect to single stuck-at-$0/1$ faults only. The design methods have yet to be adapted to other technical fault models.

1.3 ALGEBRAIC METHODS

In this section we will illustrate how such typical algebraic notions and concepts as homomorphism, algebraic operation, superposition and others can be applied in the field of error detection. It will be shown that such algebraic concepts must be adapted to concrete technical restrictions, especially to the restricted word length of the circuit considered.

1.3.1 Error Detection Using Residual Class Calculation

We shall discuss error detection by means of residual class calculation in greater detail. In principle the method is well known. Here, above all, we point out some simple characteristics of number theory that have a considerable influence on implementation.

The arithmetic operations of addition, subtraction and multiplication can, in principle, be checked in a simple way using residual class arithmetic modulo p. The operation to be checked is performed in parallel modulo p and the result is compared modulo p (cf., for example, Sellers et al., 1968). The basic circuit for checking an addition by means of residual class arithmetic modulo 3 is shown in Fig. 1.22 (cf. Langdon and Tang, 1970). The two 12-bit operands x_1 and x_2 are added in a full adder to give a 13-bit result $y = x_1 + x_2$. At the same time $x_1 \bmod 3$ and $x_2 \bmod 3$ are added in a modulo 3 adder to give $y' = (x_1 \bmod 3 + x_2 \bmod 3) \bmod 3$ and compared with $y \bmod 3 = (x_1 + x_2) \bmod 3$ in a comparator. If $y' \neq y \bmod 3$, then there is a failure in some part of the total circuitry.

The modulo 3 operation requires only the word length 2 instead of the original word length 12 of the operands x_1, x_2. ROMs (read-only memories) will be chosen as modulo-forming elements. The problem of cascadability of modulo-forming elements for larger word length operands will be discussed later.

Checking arithmetic operations of addition, subtraction and multiplication is basically simple and results from the fact that these operations in finite

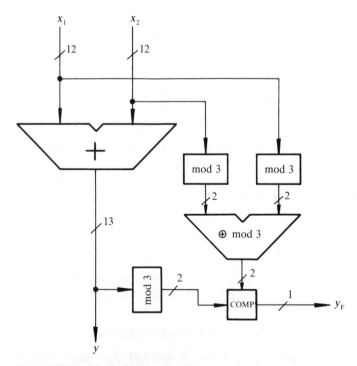

Figure 1.22 Modulo 3 checking of addition.

fields are homomorphic to the corresponding operations in the field of integers. Let a and p, $p > 0$, be integers; then, as is well known, a can be uniquely represented as

$$a = p \cdot r + s \qquad \text{with } 0 < s < p \tag{1.3}$$

We write

$$s = a \bmod p = \langle a \rangle_p \tag{1.4}$$

Here, s is the remainder of the division of a by p and r is the quotient.

For a fixed p we omit the index p in Eq. (1.4), simply writing $\langle a \rangle$. By $\langle a \rangle$ every integer a is assigned a number in the domain $0, 1, \ldots, p - 1$, namely its remainder obtained in the division by p. All integers a, a' for which $\langle a \rangle = \langle a' \rangle$ form a so-called residue class mod p. For a fixed p there exist exactly p different residue classes.

When checking arithmetic operations by means of residual class arithmetic, the equations

$$\langle x_1 + x_2 \rangle = \langle \langle x_1 \rangle + \langle x_2 \rangle \rangle$$

$$\langle x_1 - x_2 \rangle = \langle \langle x_1 \rangle - \langle x_2 \rangle \rangle$$

$$\langle x_1 \cdot x_2 \rangle = \langle \langle x_1 \rangle \cdot \langle x_2 \rangle \rangle$$

are used, where x_1 and x_2 are integers.

For special numbers p, including especially also the number 3, the formation of modulo p can be implemented in a relatively simple way. For $p = 3$ one has $4 = 2^2$ and $\langle 2^2 \rangle_3 = 1$. Thus, for any $2n$-digit binary number

$$a = a_0 + 2a_1 + 4(a_2 + 2a_3) + 4^2(a_4 + 2a_5) + \cdots + 4^{n-1}(a_{2n-2} + 2a_{2n-1})$$

one has

$$\langle a \rangle_3 = \langle \langle a_0 + 2a_1 \rangle_3 + \langle a_2 + 2a_3 \rangle_3 + \cdots + \langle a_{2n-2} + 2a_{2n-1} \rangle_3 \rangle_3$$

and a_3 can be obtained in a cascaded form by modulo 3 additions from the modulo 3 numbers $\langle a_0 + 2s_1 \rangle_3, \ldots, \langle a_{2n-2} + 2a_{2n-1} \rangle_3$. Figure 1.23 shows how the modulo 3 formation of an 8-bit binary number $a_7 a_6 a_5 a_4 a_3 a_2 a_1 a_0$ can be implemented by means of ROMs with four inputs and two outputs each.

For $p = 2^k - 1$, $k > 2$, the method just described for $k = 2$ can be generalized (cf. McClellan and Rader, 1979) since

$$\langle 2^{nk} \rangle_{2^k - 1} = 1$$

Any binary number $a = a_0 + 2a_1 + 2^2 a_2 + \cdots$ is represented as

$$a = A_0 + 2^k A_1 + 2^{2k} A_2 + \cdots$$

where

$$A_i = a_0^i + 2a_1^i + \cdots + 2^{k-1} a_{k-1}^i$$

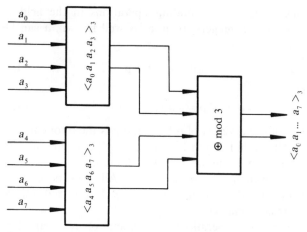

Figure 1.23 Cascaded form of modulo 3 addition.

which implies that

$$\langle a \rangle_{2^k-1} = \langle\langle A_0 \rangle + \langle A_1 \rangle + \langle A_2 \rangle + \cdots \rangle_{2^k-1}$$

For $p = 2^k + 1$ one has $\langle 2^{nk} \rangle_{2^k+1} = (-1)^n$. By analogy one finds that $\langle a \rangle_{2^k+1} = \langle\langle A_0 \rangle - \langle A_1 \rangle + \langle A_2 \rangle - \langle A_3 \rangle + \cdots \rangle_{2^k+1}$ so a cascading of the modulo formation is also possible in this case.

A slightly more difficult problem is faced when several interconnected arithmetic operations are carried out in one circuit and intermediate results must be rounded because of the limited word length available. This problem was first investigated in Smith (1980). We shall describe here an improved solution provided in Graf *et al.* (1984), with lower hardware costs than those required in Smith (1980).

If an $(r + 1)$-digit binary number $a_r \cdots a_m a_{m-1} \cdots a_0$ is rounded to an $(r + 1 - m)$-digit binary number $a'_r \cdots a'_m$, the number 2^{m-1} is added to $a_r \cdots a_0$. From the result

$$a'_r \cdots a'_m a_{m-1} a_{m-2} \cdots a_0 = a_r \cdots a_m a_{m-1} a_{m-2} \cdots a_0 + 2^{m-1} \qquad (1.5)$$

the m least significant bits are cut off. This approach is applicable to both positive and negative numbers in the twos complement representation.

The problem is to determine the value $\langle a'_r \cdots a'_m \rangle_p$ after rounding from $\langle a_r \cdots a_0 \rangle_p$ before rounding and m in a simple way. In view of Eq. (1.5) one has

$$\langle\langle a'_r \cdots a'_m \underbrace{0 \cdots 0}_{m} \rangle_p + \langle a_{m-1} a_{m-2} \cdots a_0 \rangle_p \rangle_p = \langle\langle a_r \cdots a_0 \rangle_p + \langle 2^{m-1} \rangle_p \rangle_p$$

which, because of

$$\langle a'_r \cdots a'_m \underbrace{0 \cdots 0}_{m} \rangle_p = \langle a'_r \cdots a'_m \rangle_p \cdot \langle\langle 2^m \rangle_p \rangle_p$$

with $\langle k \cdot 2^m \rangle_p = 1$, implies that

$$\langle a'_r \cdots a'_m \rangle_p = \langle k \cdot (\langle a_r \cdots a_0 \rangle_p + \langle 2^{m-1} \rangle_p - \langle a_{m-1} a_{m-2} \cdots a_0 \rangle_p) \rangle_p$$

The modulo p signal $\langle a'_r \cdots a'_m \rangle_p$ after rounding results from the modulo signal $\langle a_r \cdots a_0 \rangle_p$ before rounding by first adding the correction signal $\langle \langle 2^{m-1} \rangle_p - \langle a_{m-1} a_{m-2} \cdots a_0 \rangle_p \rangle_p$ modulo p and then multiplying the result modulo p by the number k. Here it is important that the correction signal is derived only from the m least significant bits rather than being formed over the full word length $r + 1$.

If the addition of the correction signal is implemented by a ROM, the multiplication by k can be carried out in the same ROM without additional expenditure of hardware. As an example, for a multiplication followed by rounding of the result, Fig. 1.24 shows the functional circuit for the formation of the modulo 3 value of the result after the rounding. The two 4-bit numbers x_1 and x_2 are multiplied to give an 8-bit number y, which is then rounded to a 4-bit number. The correction signal $\langle 2^3 - (y_3 y_2 y_1 y_0) \rangle_3$ is formed from the four least significant bits of the 8-bit number y and added modulo 3 to the modulo 3 signal $\langle \langle x_1 \rangle_3 \langle x_2 \rangle_3 \rangle_3$. Because $\langle 2^4 \rangle_3 = 1$ one has $k = 1$, and the multiplication by k need not be carried out explicitly.

The circuit of Fig. 1.24 is made up of ROMs with four inputs and two outputs. ROM 1 and ROM 2 act as modulo 3-forming elements, ROM 3 implements a multiplication modulo 3, ROM 4 derives the value $\langle 2^3 - (y_3 y_2 y_1 y_0) \rangle_3$ from $y_3 y_2 y_1 y_0$ and ROM 5 implements an addition modulo 3.

In this connection we draw attention to references Trautwein (1984) and Akushskij and Juditzkij (1968), where the applicability is investigated of

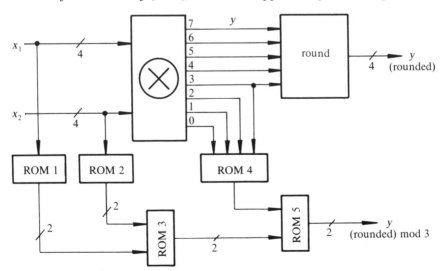

Figure 1.24 Modulo 3 checking of rounded arithmetic operations.

(inverse) residual codes to functional monitoring that is also of logical operations in an arithmetic logic unit (ALU). Another interesting possibility of error detection is given when the arithmetic operations to be monitored are generally carried out in residual class arithmetic.

A well-known fact in number theory is that every positive number z in the interval $[0, P)$ with

$$P = p_1 \cdot p_2 \cdots p_n \quad \text{with } p_i, p_j \text{ coprime for } i, j = 1, \ldots, n, i \neq j$$

can be represented in a one-to-one manner by their residual class representatives $z_1 = \langle z \rangle_{p1}, z_2 = \langle z \rangle_{p2}, \ldots, z_n = \langle z \rangle_{pn}$ (Szabo and Tanaka, 1967; Mandelbaum, 1972).

Equations (1.3), (1.4) and (1.5) hold for the addition, subtraction and multiplication of two numbers. The addition, subtraction or multiplication of two numbers corresponds with the addition, subtraction or multiplication of the representatives of these two numbers modulo p. The operations of addition, subtraction and multiplication can be carried out in parallel for the individual representatives using a reduced word length instead of full word lengths as for the original numbers.

Negative numbers handling and conversion are problems that can be mastered in principle, but require a careful approach adapted to the purpose (cf. Szabo and Tanaka, 1967; Akushakij and Juditzkij, 1968). Moreover, care should be taken not to exceed the range $[0, P)$. In this case, error detection is possible by adding further representatives (Mandelbaum, 1972; Barsi and Maestrini, 1973; Etzel and Jenkins, 1980). In particular, the following theorem is true (cf. Mandelbaum, 1972).

Let $P = p_1 \cdot p_2 \cdots p_n$, $p_i < p_{n+1}$ for $i = 1, \ldots, n$ and let the numbers p_j, p_k be coprime for $j, k = 1, \ldots, n + 1, j \neq k$. If $z \in [0, P)$, $z = (z_1, \ldots, z_i, \ldots, z_{n+1})$, $z_j = \langle z \rangle_{pj}$ for $j = 1, \ldots, n + 1$ and $\tilde{z} = (z_1, \ldots, \tilde{z}_i, \ldots, z_{n+1})$, with $z_i \neq \tilde{z}_i$, differs from z only in one component, then $\tilde{z}$ is not in the interval $[0, P)$, $\tilde{z} \notin [0, P)$.

The proof of this theorem is very simple. Obviously, for $j = 1, \ldots, n + 1$ one has

$$z = r_j \cdot p_j + z_j$$

$$\tilde{z} = r'_j \cdot p_j + z'_j$$

where $z'_j = z_j$ for $j \neq i$, $z'_i = \tilde{z}_i \neq z_i$ and $z \neq \tilde{z}$, from which it follows for $j \neq i$ that $(\tilde{z} - z) = (r'_j - r_j) \cdot p_j$. Since for $j \neq i$ it follows that p_j is a divisor of $\tilde{z} - z$, the least common multiple of the numbers $p_1, \ldots, p_{i-1}, p_{i+1}, \ldots, p_{n+1}$. which equals their product in this case, is a divisor of $\tilde{z} - z$. Since $z \in [0, P)$, it then follows that $\tilde{z} \notin [0, P)$.

Consequently, if one describes numbers belonging to an interval $[0, P)$ in a redundant representation system $p_1, \ldots, p_n$, p_{n+1} with the additional representative p_{n+1}, then every error that changes only one representative causes the erroneous number to lie outside the interval $[0, P)$. For error detection, one has then only to determine whether a number z is in the interval $[0, P)$, which is frequently done by converting the residual class representation into a mixed positional number system (mixed radix conversion), with z represented as

$$z = a_0 + a_1 \cdot p_1 + a_2 \cdot p_1 \cdot p_2 + \cdots + a_n \cdot p_1 \cdot p_2 \cdots p_n$$

where

$$a_0 < p_1, a_1 < p_2, \ldots, a_n < p_{n+1}$$

(cf. Mandelbaum, 1972). In terms of hardware, this conversion requires a relatively high expenditure.

Extensive special literature deals with fast (parallel) and economical implementation of this method. Here we refer only to Huang (1983), Jenkins and Altman (1983) and Jenkins (1983).

1.3.2 Error Detection by Superposition

For an overall system consisting of n, $n > 2$, linear stable automata L over a field K in series with a threshold element Thr, the generalized superposition principle (Gössel, 1982) can be used for on-line error detection. The automaton L is described by the equations

$$z(t + 1) = A \cdot z(t) + B \cdot x(t)$$

$$y(t) = C \cdot z(t) + D \cdot x(t)$$

where x, y, z are the input, output and state vectors and A, B, C, D are matrices of corresponding dimensions with elements of K. Because of the assumed stability, i.e. because of $\lim A^t = 0$, for the automaton L one has the following input/output (I/O) formula:

$$y(t) = \sum_{i=0}^{t} H(t - i) \cdot x(i) \quad \text{with} \quad H(\tau) = \begin{cases} D & \text{for } \tau = 0 \\ CA^{-1}B & \text{for } \tau > 0 \end{cases} \quad (1.6)$$

(for details, see, for example, Gill, 1966). The threshold elements implements a combinational function Thr: $Y \to \{0, 1\}$, with

$$\text{Thr}(y) = \begin{cases} 1 & \text{for } y \geqslant s \\ 0 & \text{for } y < s \end{cases}$$

where s is the threshold value. Without loss of generality it can be assumed that the threshold is in the middle of all possible input values (Gössel and Rebel, 1984). The element can then be a majority element. Figure 1.25 shows the overall system.

The superposition properties for the linear automaton L follow immediately from the linearity of the input/output formula (1.6). If, for a sufficiently large t, the following relation holds for the input of another linear

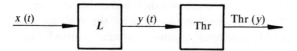

Figure 1.25 Serial connection of linear automation and threshold function.

automaton:

$$x_{n+1}(t) = \sum_{j=1}^{n} a_j x_j(t)$$

then, in view of Eq. (1.6), it follows that

$$y_{n+1}(t) = \sum_{i=0}^{t} H(t-i) \cdot \sum_{j=1}^{n} a_j x_j(i) = \sum_{j=1}^{n} a_j y_j(t)$$

The threshold function Thr defines on Y a classification into the classes K_0 and K_1 by

$$K_0 = \{y/\mathrm{Thr}(y) = 0\}$$
$$K_1 = \{y/\mathrm{Thr}(y) = 1\}$$

On the classes K_0 and K_1, an arbitrary binary operation $\bigcirc$ is defined. If one states

$$u \bigtriangledown u' = \Phi(\Phi^{-1}(u) \bigcirc \Phi^{-1}(u'))$$

where

$$\Phi(K_0) = 0, \qquad \Phi(K_1) = 1, \qquad \Phi^{-1}(0) = K_0, \qquad \Phi^{-1}(1) = K_1$$

then obviously one has

$$\Phi(K_u) \bigtriangledown \Phi(K_{u'}) = \Phi(K_u \bigcirc K_{u'})$$

If we now define a binary operation $\bullet$ on Y such that

$$K_{\mathrm{Thr}(y)} \bigcirc K_{\mathrm{Thr}(y')} = K_{\mathrm{Thr}(y \bullet y')}$$

is satisfied, then Thr is ($\bullet$, $\bigtriangledown$) superponable, since

$$\mathrm{Thr}(y \bullet y') = \Phi(K_{\mathrm{Thr}(y \bullet y')}) = \Phi(K_{\mathrm{Thr}(y)}) \bigcirc (K_{\mathrm{Thr}(y')})$$
$$= \Phi(\Phi^{-1}(\mathrm{Thr}(y)) \bigcirc \Phi^{-1}(\mathrm{Thr}(y'))) = \mathrm{Thr}(y) \bigtriangledown \mathrm{Thr}(y')$$

We set

$$K_0 \bigcirc K_0 = K_1 \bigcirc K_1 = K_0, \qquad K_0 \bigcirc K_1 = K_1 \bigcirc K_0 = K_1$$

and hence $0 \bigtriangledown 0 = 1 \bigtriangledown 1 = 0, 1 \bigtriangledown 0 = 0 \bigtriangledown 1 = 1$, and the operations $\bigcirc$ and $\bigtriangledown$ are isomorphic with the addition modulo 2. For the numbers $0, 1, \ldots, 7$ and the threshold $\mathrm{Thr} = 3$ one obtains

$$K_0 = \{0, 1, 2, 3\}, \qquad K_1 = \{4, 5, 6, 7\}$$

Table 1.6

	0	1	2	3	4	5	6	7
1			B			A		
1	K_0				K_1			
2								
3								
4			C			D		
5	K_1				K_0			
6								
7								

If the operation $\bullet$ is so defined that the boxes denoted by A, B, C, D in Table 1.6 contain only elements of K_1, K_0, K_1 and K_0, respectively, then Thr is ($\bullet$, $\triangledown$) superponable. Obviously there are different operations $\bullet$ with this property. If the numbers 0, 1, 2, ..., 7 are coded as three-digit binary numbers and if the operation $\bullet$ is defined as a component-wise EXCLUSIVE-OR operation, then the conditions formulated by Table 1.6 are satisfied. Like the operation $\bigcirc$, the operation $\bullet$ is uniquely solvable for both variables and, moreover, is associative. To illustrate this, the validity of the superposition principle for the threshold function means that the circuits of Fig. 1.26 are equivalent.

Now let us discuss error detection by means of the circuit shown in Fig. 1.27. The error detection is performed separately for the linear part and the threshold function. In this way the most favourable properties of these two functional elements (linearity, combinational function) can be optimally utilized for error detection.

The circuit detects each single functional error.

1. At some time, L_k outputs the value $y_k'(t)$ instead of $y_k(t)$, $1 \leqslant k \leqslant n$. Since $\sum_j a_j y_j \neq \sum_{j \neq k} a_j y_j + a_k y_k'$, the signals appearing at the outputs I and II do not agree and the comparator indicates an error.

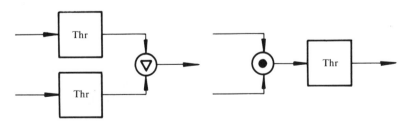

Figure 1.26 Superposition principle for a threshold function.

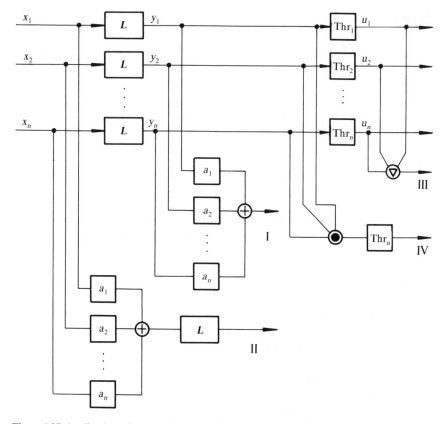

Figure 1.27 Application of superposition principle to error detection.

2. At some time, the circuit Thr_k outputs the value $u'_k = \bar{u}_k$ instead of u_k. This error is also detected immediately, because $u_1 \triangledown u_2 \triangledown \cdots \triangledown u_k \triangledown \cdots \triangledown u_n \neq u_1 \triangledown u_2 \triangledown \cdots \triangledown \bar{u}_k \triangledown \cdots \triangledown u_n$, and hence the signals appearing at the outputs III and IV do not agree and a comparator indicates an error.

1.3.3 Use of Pair Algebras

For an arbitrary given automaton $A = (X, Y, Z, g, f)$, a reduced monitoring automaton $A_k = (X_k, Y_k, Z_k, g_k, f_k)$ is determined in Danilov et al. (1975). This detects any error with a Hamming weight less than or equal to d of the binary-coded state vector of A or A_k or of the output of A or A_k at the time of its first occurrence. Here d may be given, where d also determines the complexity of the checking circuit. The design of the checking circuit is shown in Fig. 1.28.

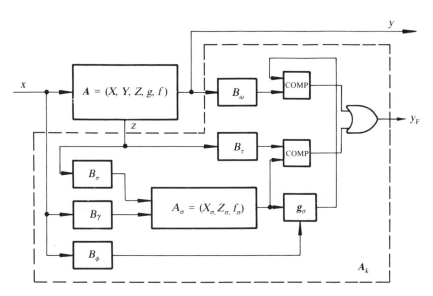

Figure 1.28 Application of pair algebras to error detection.

The set of inputs to the monitoring automaton A_k is $X \times Z$. The automaton A_k is determined by the choice of partition pairs (γ, τ), (π, τ), (τ, ω), (φ, ω) from the pair algebras $\Delta_{xz}, \Delta_{zz}, \Delta_{zy}, \Delta_{xy}$ according to Hartmanis and Stearns (1966) and by the automaton A. The blocks B_π, B_γ, B_φ, B_ω, B_τ each assign to their inputs the partitions of their respective input sets containing these inputs. The semi-automaton A_σ and the function g_σ provide a coarse simulation of the behaviour of A. Owing to the additional input of z into the monitoring automaton, the latter cannot simply be described as a homomorphism of A, although it is very similar to a homomorphism. The comparators COMP, whose outputs are fed to an OR gate, output 0 if their inputs agree and 1 if they do not.

Details, especially concerning the coding of states required to ensure the error detection properties, the possible addition of further outputs to A and the choice of suitable partition pairs are given in Danilov *et al.* (1975). In our opinion the described approach has the following disadvantages:

1. The error detection properties can only be graduated coarsely. Only the Hamming weight of the errors to be detected can be selected as a parameter of the error detection circuit. This makes the error detection circuit rather complex and only able to be coarsely graduated.
2. The states of the automaton A to be monitored must be available to the monitoring automaton. In order for this requirement to be satisfied, additional outputs of the automaton A are generally necessary.

The requirement that a considered state failure should be detected immediately rather than after its first effect on the output also adds to the expenditure required for error detection. It should be pointed out that in this work an algebraic approach to error detection for arbitrary sequential automata is given. Starting from the investigation of separable discrete systems, another algebraically founded method of error detection is presented in Danilov and Shibarok (1986), which, however, does not use a technological failure model.

1.4 DETECTION OF SEQUENCE ERRORS

The detection of sequence errors is a borderline problem of on-line error detection. System properties that are known with certainty to lead to an incorrect input/output behaviour or have a high probability of doing so are monitored during normal operation of the system without checking the actual input/output behaviour of the system.

A frequently used method of detecting sequence errors is the so-called operation-time checking. It is applicable if one can derive the structure of the data or circuitry of the system from the type of sequences where specific events must succeed one another, at least within a certain interval, or where operations must be finished within a certain time. The error signal is derived by comparing signals of the event control with a time reference. The simplest example is a watch-dog timer in bus-based computer systems. A great variety of technical solutions exist for this approach, which depend on the actual system. We refer to Stodola (1982) as an example.

Other types of sequence monitoring refer to discovering forbidden control states. Thus the one-to-one property of transmitter-to-receiver relations is checked—for instance, whether several transmitters are transmitting simultaneously to a bidirectional data bus or whether a register is loaded simultaneously from several sources (McPherson, 1973). In many storage circuits it is not possible to execute a read and a write access at the same time. A suitable checking circuit can then monitor compliance with this condition.

The compression of a given data sequence to a signature is known as signature analysis in circuitry testing and can be used for the error detection of given sequences. In Olah (1973) it has been proposed that during the execution of a program the currently active instructions of the program, being encoded as binary words, are added up to a test sum in an adder accumulator and that at certain points of the program the actual sum obtained is compared with its precalculated reference value. If the actual value differs from the reference value, an error is indicated. For a program loop for which the number of loop runs is unknown, an additional value is added to the sum so that the sum over the instruction words of the loop plus the additional value give zero.

In a simple program branching where the different branches rejoin, a correction value equalling the difference between the sums of the instruction words of the different branches is added to one branch. This ensures that the test sum does not depend on how often loops are executed in a program or which of the branches are executed. Variable data to be processed or calculated by the program are not included in the test sums, so in this case only the instructions stored in the main memory are checked. A possible error, if any, is detected at the fixed reference points, but in general only after some time has elapsed.

Monitoring the transfer of blocks of interrelated data by the same principle is described in Peterson (1983). Instead of the adder accumulator, Proto (1978) describes the use of a linear n-digit shift register with m inputs, to which the known sequence of m-digit binary words to be monitored, $m + 1 < n$, is input with word length m. The state of the feedback shift register reached after a given number of inputs is compared with a precalculated value. Unlike the adder accumulator, the state of the feedback shift register also depends on the order of succession of the inputted binary words. By a suitable choice of the feedback logic the register can be modified so that some errors are detected with certainty. Also, in this case errors are detected after a time delay.

Monitoring the data transfer via bidirectional data paths raises special problems (bus structure). This is true especially if the individual bus subscribers are separately operating units (e.g. processors of a multiprocessor system or units connected to an I/O channel of an electronic data processing (EDP) computer). In this case, methhods of sequence monitoring frequently make it possible for a standardized error detection strategy to be introduced in the overall system; this can be followed by all subscribers, however different their circuit structure may be (see, for instance, Flinders et al., 1972; Lee, 1984).

Let us further point out the method described in Hartung et al. (1984), which is an interesting variant of the method used to detect sequence errors. It serves to monitor the addressing in block-wise data transfers from mass storage into an operational store. The K data items of the transferred block are secured by L check items of a code, so that storing one block initially requires $K + L$ addresses. For the storage of each block, however, a storage area of $K + L + 1$ is provided, so that the last address of the area provided for a block is not occupied by data. Unless after reading the $K + L$ addresses of a block a new starting address of a new block is loaded into the address register, the $K + L$ following addresses, starting from the last address of the preceding block, are read out. The error-detecting code now generally detects an error, because the present last L data have not been calculated by encoding the preceding K data. Therefore, loading the address register after a block end is also monitored by the error-detecting code.

1.5 SPECIAL ERROR DETECTION CIRCUITS

In Hong $et\ al.$ (1973), for a combinational circuit f_s implementing the function f, an error detection circuit F_s taking into account the error model of f_s is stated by means of a one-implicant I_1 of f (1-cover) and a zero-implicant I_0 of f (0-cover), which is described below.

Let f be a Boolean function of n arguments, $f: \{0, 1\}^n \to \{0, 1\}$, $n = 1$. I_1 is called a one-implicant of f if, for every bit combination $x_1^*, \ldots, x_n^* \in \{0, 1\}^n$, $I_1(x_1^*, \ldots, x_n^*) = 1$ implies that $f(x_1^*, \ldots, x_n^*) = 1$. I_0 is called a zero-implicant of f if, for every bit combination $x_1^*, \ldots, x_n^* \in \{0, 1\}^n$, $I_0(x_1^*, \ldots, x_n^*) = 1$ implies that $f(x_1^*, \ldots, x_n^*) = 0$.

Obviously f is a one-implicant of f and $\bar{f}$ is a zero-implicant of f. If $I_1(x_1^*, \ldots, x_n^*) = 1$ for a bit combination $x_1^*, \ldots, x_n^*$ and if f_s output the value 0 when this bit pattern was applied, then there was a failure in f_s. On the other hand, if $I_0(x_1^*, \ldots, x_n^*) = 1$ and f_s outputs the value 1, then there is also a failure in f_s. With the assumption that I_1 and I_0 are unfaulted, f_s is at least faulty if

$$\bar{y} \wedge I_1 \vee y \wedge I_0 = 1$$

with $y = f_s(x_1, \ldots, x_n)$. For the bit combination $x_1^*, \ldots, x_n^*$ for which $I_1(x_1^*, \ldots, x_n^*) = I_0(x_1^*, \ldots, x_n^*) = 0$, one has, independently of the value of y,

$$\bar{y} \wedge I_1 \vee y \wedge I_0 = 0 \vee 0 = 0$$

The error detection circuit F_s derived from these considerations for monitoring f_s is shown in Fig. 1.29. For $I_1 = f$ and $I_0 = \bar{f}$, the circuit of Fig. 1.29 is equivalent, with duplication of the circuit F_s and comparison of the outputs, because

$$\bar{f}_s \wedge f \vee f_s \wedge \bar{f} = f_s \oplus f$$

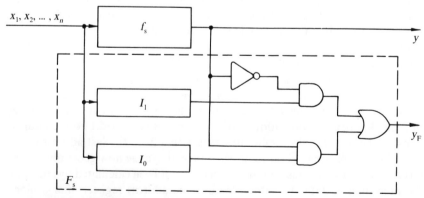

Figure 1.29 Error detection by covers.

The essential ideas of Hong *et al.* (1973) consist of the fact that I_1 and I_0 are so chosen that they can easily be implemented. In return it is accepted that only part of the possible failures of f_s are detected. In practice, the approach used in Hong *et al.* (1973) is to first determine the prime implicants of the canonical disjunctive normal forms of f and $\bar{f}$. Then I_1 is determined as a disjunctive combination of a subset of prime implicants of f and I_0 as a disjunctive combination of a subset of prime implicants of $\bar{f}$. These subsets are fixed step by step so that in each step as many stuck-at-0 and stuck-at-1 errors as possible of the function f implemented as a disjunctive normal form are detected. The number of steps depends on the amount of expenditure acceptable for error detection and on the percentage of errors of the error model that is to be detected.

In Tomlin (1970) an error detection circuit for a digital frequency divider is given which, when a failure affects the output of the frequency divider, outputs an error signal within a certain delay rather than immediately. This, as well as skilful utilization of the special properties of a frequency divider, makes it possible to keep hardware complexity relatively low.

The frequency divider transforms a binary sequence $x_1 x_2 x_3 \cdots$ into a binary sequence $y_1 y_2 y_3 \cdots$, with

$$y_t = \begin{cases} 1 & \text{for } \sum_{i=1}^{t} x_i = k \cdot n, k > 0 \\ 0 & \text{otherwise} \end{cases}$$

so that S_n outputs a one after each input of n ones, and zeros otherwise. The corresponding error detection circuit consists of two identical frequency dividers S_m^1, S_m^2 and a Boolean function f and is shown in Fig. 1.30. The input of the frequency divider S_n is interconnected with the input of the frequency divider S_m^1, and the output of S_n is connected to the input of S_m^2. The two outputs of S_m^1 and S_m^2 are the inputs to the Boolean function f, at the output of which the error signal appears.

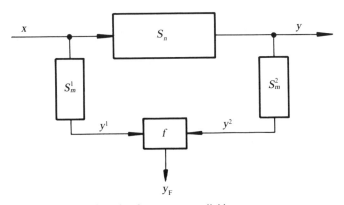

Figure 1.30 Error detection for a sequence divider.

Table 1.7

x	1	0	1	1	1	0	1	1	1	1	1	0	1	0	0	1	1	1	0	0
y	0	0	0	1	0	0	0	0	1	0	0	0	0	0	0	1	0	0	0	0
y^1	0	0	0	1	0	0	0	1	0	0	1	0	0	0	0	1	1	0	0	0
y^2	0	0	0	1	0	0	0	0	0	0	0	0	0	0	0	0	0	0	0	0
$f(y^1,y^2)$	0	0	0	0	0	0	0	0	0	0	0	0	0	0	0	0	0	0	0	0
y	0	0	1	0	0	0	0	1	0	0	0	0	1	0	0	0	0	0	0	0
y^2	0	0	1	0	0	0	0	0	0	0	0	0	0	0	0	0	0	0	0	0
$f(y^1,y^2)$	0	0	1	0	0	0	0	0	0	0	0	0	0	0	0	0	0	0	0	0

Upon input of $x_1, x_2, x_3, \ldots, S_m^1$ outputs the binary sequence $y_1^1, y_2^2, y_3^3, \ldots$, with

$$y_t^1 = \begin{cases} 1 & \text{for } \sum_{i=1}^t x_i = h \cdot m, h > 0 \\ 0 & \text{otherwise} \end{cases}$$

Since m and n are coprime, S_n and S_m^1, provided they are operating correctly, output a 1 simultaneously iff

$$\sum_{i=1}^1 x_i = j \cdot m \cdot n \qquad \text{for } j > 0$$

This is the case iff $k = j \cdot m$ or iff S_m^2 outputs a 1 upon input of the binary sequence $y_1 y_2 \cdots$.

For the function f one has

$$f(y^1, y^2) = \bar{y}^1 \wedge y^2$$

and hence $f(0, 0) = f(1, 0) = f(1, 1) = 0$ and $f(0, 1) = 1$, so that an error is indicated iff S_m^2 outputs a one and S_m^1 outputs a zero. Erroneous outputs y of the frequency divider S_n for which

$$y = 1 \text{ with } \sum_{i=1}^\tau x_i = k \cdot n + d, \qquad d \neq l \cdot n, k, l > 0$$

are detected when S_m^2 outputs the next 1, i.e. not later than after the input of $n \cdot m$ ones into S_n. For large n and small m the error detection circuit requires less expenditure than duplication and comparison. Modifications of the circuit shown in Fig. 1.30 are described in Tomlin (1970).

For the example, $n = 4, m = 3$, the operation of the error detection circuit is shown in Table 1.7 for a correct and an error variant. The erroneous signals and the error indication are shown in bold type.

The method proposed in Umo and Ikuro (1980) for monitoring an interface between a microcomputer with a multicomponent output and a system to be controlled by this computer takes an intermediate position between testing and on-line error detection. The microcomputer periodically outputs only ones or only zeros on all of its output lines over very short time intervals, and on the output lines of the interface it is checked whether all the lines are in the state 1 or 0 in the corresponding time intervals. These time intervals for testing the interface are periodically inserted in the normal operation of the microcomputer. The length of the test intervals is so small that the system to be controlled does not respond to pulses of this duration.

1.6 SUMMARY

In this first chapter we have described a variety of known, quite different methods for the design of error detection circuits. The simplest method is that of circuit duplication and comparison of the outputs. Two-rail logic, pseudo-duplication and regeneration of the input symbols are modifications of this principle. In two-rail logic the original circuit and its duplicate are designed using a logic that includes inverse outputs; therefore, in the overall circuit all signals always occur in both the proper and the inverted form. In the case of pseudo-duplication the data are processed twice in succession by the same circuit, but along different data paths, and are then checked for equality. For a circuit that has an inverse circuit the method of regeneration of the inputs can be applied. The inputs of the monitored circuit are regenerated from the outputs by the inverse circuit of the original circuit. The original inputs and the regenerated inputs can then be compared. Although the method of duplication and comparison and the corresponding modifications are basically simple, a disadvantage of these methods is that the full error-detecting circuit is more than twice the size of the monitored circuit.

The coding methods developed in communications engineering have been designed for the detection of single-bit errors or some error bursts on communication channels. They can be applied without any particular problems to the monitoring of data paths and memories. However, in most circuits even single failures of the components may cause quite different functional errors in several bits. This is the reason why problems arise in the application of error detection codes to error detection in random logic. For special circuits with a simple functional description of their behaviour, such as adders and decoders, coding methods are also practicable. Special codes such as arithmetic codes for adders were developed for these circuits. Coding methods may also be applied for monitoring regular circuits or specially designed circuits, such as circuits with completely independent bits or independent slices of bits.

Self-checking circuits indicate their own faults during normal operation. In the fault-free case they map input code words into output code words. A non-code output of a self-checking circuit indicates either a fault in the circuit or a non-code (erroneous) input. One of the problems arises from the fact that all faults considered must be detected by error-free input code words. In the case of embedded circuits it can not always be guaranteed that all fault-free input code words necessary for the error detection actually occur. Essential parts of general self-checking circuits are self-checking code checkers and self-checking comparators. Quite different implementations of self-checking comparators are also presented in this chapter.

The algebraic concepts of homomorphism, superposition, pair-algebras and others can also be applied in the field of error detection. As an example, the quite simple possibility of checking the arithmetic operations of addition, subtraction and multiplication by the use of residual class calculations modulo p has been discussed in detail. This possibility results from the fact that the operations, addition modulo p, subtraction modulo p and multiplication modulo p, are homomorphic to the corresponding operation in the field of integers. It has been shown how the results of computations in modulo p have to be corrected if the results of the integer computations are to be rounded because of the restricted word length available.

The application of a generalized superposition principle has been demonstrated for a system consisting of a linear automaton in series with a threshold element. The detection of sequence errors has also been considered. As well as the well-known principles of error detection, we have also described the most interesting of the sometimes ingenious solutions for optimal design of error detection circuits, which have been explained until now only in patent applications. By including these little known patents, we hope that the reader will now have a clear impression of the current state of the art in error detection and of the variety of novel ideas and methods that have evolved in this rapidly growing field. However, we also hope that the reader has gained an impression of what has been missing until now: a theory for the systematic design of error detection circuits for an arbitrarily given combinational or sequential circuit with an arbitrarily specified fault model. Such a theory will be presented in Chapter 2 for combinational circuits and in Chapter 3 for sequential circuits.

COMBINATIONAL ERROR DETECTION CIRCUITS

In the first chapter we have outlined typical principles and examples of known error detection circuits. As we have seen, relatively good solutions are known for special circuits with a simple functional behaviour such as adders, decoders, comparators, sequence dividers and others, but not for random logic. It can be seen that until now all these solutions have not been optimally adapted to the technical faults of the monitored circuit and that the error detection circuits are not systematically designed. In this chapter we will describe a systematic method of designing combinational error detection circuits for arbitrarily chosen combinational circuits. The previously described examples, such as duplication and comparison, regeneration of input symbols and application of codes, are special cases of this method insofar as the erroneous circuit remains a combinational one.

The method is effective in detecting faults from a given set of technical faults. The fault set is determined by the technology used and is specified by the designer. An error function can be formally assigned to every fault of the fault set considered. In this way the error function corresponding to a given fault is the function implemented by the combinational circuit in the presence of the fault. Thus the fault set can be functionally described by a set of error functions.

The error detection circuit detects if the circuit exhibits an incorrect output for the first time, which is a possible output of an error function in the functional error model. For other incorrect outputs that are not outputs of any error function of the error model, the error detection circuit remains undetermined and in the first step the error detection circuit is a partially determined combinational circuit. This fact will be described by corresponding don't-care conditions, which can be used to optimize the error detection circuit. Optimization of the partially determined combinational circuit must be done using computer aided design (CAD) tools of the designer. Thus for a given circuit to be monitored and for a specified set of technical faults, the proposed method is optimal, that is if the applied optimization procedure results in an optimal solution. All the faults of the specified fault model are immediately detected when they influence the output of the monitored circuit for the first time. All the don't-care conditions are used for optimization of the error detection circuit. Thus we assume that the error detection circuit works correctly.

The method described is applied to the design of error detection circuits for binary adders using different error models. The detection of all single errors of a combinational circuit according to Sogomonyan (1970) is considered in detail as well as the different weakening requirements needed to further reduce the overheads for error detection.

2.1 BASIC CONCEPTS

Let f_s be a combinational circuit used to implement a combinational function $f: X \to Y$ with the error model $F(f) = \{f_0, f_1, \ldots, f_n\}$. For the standard function f_0 one has $f_0 = f$. The functions $f_1, \ldots, f_n$ of the error model are functions that may be implemented instead of f by the circuit f_s when the technological failures that are considered occur. They are called error functions. $X \subseteq X$ is the subset of inputs for which the behaviour of f_s is of interest. A more detailed description of the functional error model of a circuit is given in the Appendix. Then the function $\phi: X \times Y \to \{0, 1\}$ defined by

$$\phi(x, y) = \begin{cases} 0 & \text{for } x \in X \text{ and } y = f(x) = f_0(x) \\ 1 & \text{for } x \in X \text{ and } \exists f_i \in F(f), \text{with } y = f_i(x) \neq f(x) \\ -(\text{don't care}) & \text{otherwise} \end{cases}$$

$$(2.1)$$

is called the error detection function of f with the error model $F(f)$. A technical implementation ϕ_s of ϕ is called an error detection circuit of f_s with the error model $F(f)$. Of practical interest is the case $X = \{0, 1\}^n$, $Y = \{0, 1\}^m$, $n, m > 0$, so that $\phi(x, y)$ is a partially defined Boolean function of $(n + m)$ variables.

The block diagram of the combinational circuit f_s to be monitored and of the corresponding error detection circuit ϕ_s is shown in Fig. 2.1. ϕ_s outputs the value $y_F = 0$ if f_s implements the standard function f. If f_s implements one of the functions f_i of the error model and if $f(x) \neq f_i(x)$ for the applied input x, then ϕ_s outputs the value $y_F = 1$.

For errors that do not belong to the error model considered, the error detection function ϕ is not defined (don't care). The don't-care conditions of the function ϕ are used to optimize the error detection circuit.

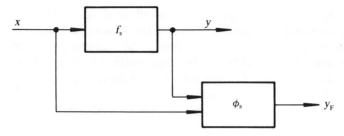

Figure 2.1 Combinational circuit f_s monitored by error detection circuit ϕ_s.

The hardware costs required for an error detection circuit determined by Eq. (2.1) can never exceed that for duplication and comparison. If we fix all the don't-care conditions in (2.1) at 1 and do not restrict the input set of the combinational circuit f_s, then for the error detection function we have

$$\phi(x, y) = \begin{cases} 0 & \text{for } x \in X \text{ and } y = f(x) \\ 1 & \text{for } x \in X \text{ and } y \neq f(x) \end{cases} \tag{2.2}$$

The error detection function ϕ for which Eq. (2.2) holds true can be implemented by duplication and comparison, as shown in Fig. 2.2. The comparator shown in Fig. 2.2 outputs the value 0 if both of its inputs are equal and 1 if its inputs are different. Utilizing the don't-care conditions in Eq. (2.1), one generally obtains much smaller favourable solutions than by duplication and comparison.

The design of an on-line error detection circuit can be performed for a combinational circuit in the following steps:

1. Choose the input set $X \subseteq X$ of interest.
2. Choose an error model $F(f)$ based on the component failures to be expected.
3. Determine the table of values of the error detection function ϕ: $X \times Y \rightarrow \{0, 1\}$.
4. Optimization (minimization) of the partially defined function.
5. Implementation of the optimized function ϕ by a circuit ϕ_s.

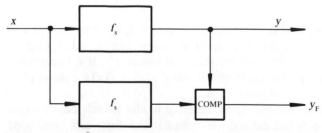

Figure 2.2 Duplication and comparison of a combinational circuit f_s.

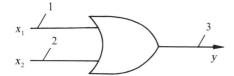

Figure 2.3 OR gate.

Let us now illustrate the basic idea, described above, for determination of an error detection circuit by a very simple example. Determine an error detection circuit for the combinational circuit f_s, which implements the binary Boolean function $f(x_1, x_2) = x_1 \vee x_2$ (disjunction). We suppose here $X = \{00, 01, 10, 11\}$. Figure 2.3 shows an OR gate. The input and output lines of the OR gate are numbered from 1 to 3.

The functional error model $F(x_1 \vee x_2)$ of the OR gate is determined by the technical faults considered. In the first case we suppose that only stuck-at-1 faults at one of the input lines 1 or 2 or at the output line 3 may occur. In all these cases the faulty OR element implements the constant function $f_1(x_1 \vee x_2) = 1$ instead of $x_1 \vee x_2$. If only stuck-at-1 faults of the input and output lines are taken into account, the corresponding functional error model F_1 is

$$F_1(x_1 \wedge x_2) = \{f_0(x_1, x_2) = x_1 \vee x_2, f_1(x_1, x_2) = 1\}$$

Now the error detection function $\phi_1(x_1, x_2, y)$ has to be determined. According to Eq. (2.1) we have

$$\phi_1(x_1, x_2, y) = \begin{cases} 0 & \text{for } y = x_1 \vee x_2 \\ 1 & \text{for } y = 1 \neq x_1 \vee x_2 \\ -\text{(don't care)} & \text{otherwise} \end{cases}$$

The tables of the values for the functions f_0, f_1 and ϕ_1 are shown in Table 2.1. For $y = x_1 \vee x_2$ we have $\phi_1(x_1, x_2, y) = 0$ (rows 1, 4, 6, 8). The only row with $y = 1 \neq x_1 \vee x_2$ and therefore $\phi_1(x_1, x_2, y) = 1$ is the row 2.

Table 2.1

x_1	x_2	y	$x_1 \vee x_2$	$1(f_1)$	ϕ_1	Row
0	0	0	0	1	0	1
0	0	1	0	1	1	2
0	1	0	1	1	—	3
0	1	1	1	1	0	4
1	0	0	1	1	—	5
1	0	1	1	1	0	6
1	1	0	1	1	—	7
1	1	1	1	1	0	8

In all other cases (rows 3, 5, 7) the function $\phi_1(x_1, x_2, y)$ remains undetermined. This is due to the fact that the corresponding errors are not errors of the error model that is considered. Thus for $x_1 = 0$, $x_2 = 1$ the output of f_s cannot be $y = 0$ if only stuck-at-1 faults of the input lines or of the output line may occur (row 3).

The same arguments are true for $x_1 = 1$, $x_2 = 0$, $y = 0$ (row 5) and $x_1 = x_2 = 1$, $y = 0$ (row 7). The don't-care conditions can be used to optimize the error detection function ϕ_1. A concrete solution is

$$\phi_1(x_1, x_2, y) = \bar{x}_1 \wedge \bar{x}_2 \wedge y = \overline{x_1 \vee x_2 \vee \bar{y}}$$

Now we consider the case of stuck-at-0 faults. In the case of a stuck-at-0 fault of the lines 1, 2 or 3 the OR element implements the functions $f'_1(x_1, x_2) = 0 \vee x_2 = x_2$, $f'_2(x_1, x_2) = x_1 \vee 0 = x_1$ and $f'_3(x_1, x_2) = 0$ respectively. The functional error model F_0 is therefore

$$F_0(x_1 \vee x_2) = \{x_1 \vee x_2, x_2, x_1, 0\}$$

The functions x_1, x_2, 0 are the error functions of the OR gate caused by technical stuck-at-0 faults. According to Eq. (2.1), for the error detection function ϕ_0 we have

$$\phi_0(x_1, x_2, y) =$$

$$\begin{cases} 0 & \text{for } y = x_1 \vee x_2 \\ 1 & \text{for } (y = x_1 \text{ or } y = x_2 \text{ or } y = 0) \text{ and } y \neq x_1 \vee x_2 \\ - \text{ (don't care)} & \text{otherwise} \end{cases}$$

Table 2.2 shows the values for the error functions f_0, f'_1, f'_2, f'_3 and the error detection function ϕ_0. For $y = x_1 \vee x_2$ we again have $\phi_0(x_1, x_2, y) = 0$ (rows 1, 4, 6, 8). Row 3 describes the case $y \neq x_1 \vee x_2$ and $y = x_1$ or $y = 0$. Therefore the error functions x_1 and 0 are given in this row. Analogously, in row 5 we have $y \neq x_1 \vee x_2$, $y = x_2$ or $y = 0$ with the error functions x_2, 0; in row 7, $y \neq x_1 \vee x_2$ and $y = 0$ with the error function 0. In row 2, $\phi_0(x_1, x_2, y)$ remains undetermined. Although we have $y \neq x_1 \vee x_2$ there is no error function f'_i of the considered error model F_0 for which we had

$$1 = f'_i(0, 0), \qquad f'_i \in F_0(x_1 \vee x_2)$$

A possible solution for ϕ_0 is

$$\phi_0(x_1, x_2, y) = \bar{y}(x_1 \vee x_2)$$

If we assume now that stuck-at-0 faults as well as stuck-at-1 faults of the lines 1, 2, 3 of the OR gate occur, the functional error model becomes

$$F_{0,1} = F_0 \cup F_1 = \{x_1 \vee x_2, x_2, x_1, 0, 1\}$$

Table 2.2

x_1	x_2	y	f_0 $x_1 \vee x_2$	f_1' x_2	f_2' x_1	f_3' 0	$\phi_0(x_1, x_2, y)$	Row	Error function
0	0	0	0	0	0	0	0	1	
0	0	1	0	0	0	0	—	2	—
0	1	0	1	1	0	0	1	3	$x_1, 0$
0	1	1	1	1	0	0	0	4	
1	0	0	1	0	1	0	1	5	$x_2, 0$
1	0	1	1	0	1	0	0	6	
1	1	0	1	1	1	0	1	7	0
1	1	1	1	1	1	0	0	8	

Table 2.3

x_1	x_3	y	$\phi_{0,1}(x_1, x_2, y)$	Error function
0	0	0	0	
0	0	1	1	1
0	1	0	1	$x_1, 0$
0	1	1	0	
1	0	0	1	$x_2, 0$
1	0	1	0	
1	1	0	1	0
1	1	1	0	

and the corresponding error detection function $\phi_{0,1}$ is determined by

$\phi_{0,1}(x_1, x_2, y) =$

$$\begin{cases} 0 & \text{for } y = x_1 \vee x_2 \\ 1 & \text{for } (y = x_1 \text{ or } y = x_2 \text{ or } y = 0 \text{ or } y = 1) \text{ and } y \neq x_1 \vee x_2 \\ \text{—(don't care)} & \text{otherwise} \end{cases}$$

Table 2.3 shows that $\phi_{0,1}$ is completely defined and that we have

$$\phi_{0,1}(x_1, x_2, y) = \begin{cases} 0 & \text{for } y = x_1 \vee x_2 \\ 1 & \text{for } y \neq x_1 \vee x_2 \end{cases}$$

and $\phi_{0,1}$ is then equivalent to duplication and comparison of the original circuit.

The definition of an error detection circuit for a combinational circuit includes the known type solutions as special cases, which will be illustrated by the following examples of 'separate processing of check symbols' according to Geisselhardt (1978) and 'error detection by codes'.

The separate processing of check symbols, shown schematically in Fig. 2.4, leads to the functional equation

$$g(a(x_1), b(x_2)) = c(f(x_1, x_2)) \tag{2.3}$$

where the function f to be implemented is given. For function f, functions a, b, c and g that satisfy Eq. (2.3) are to be determined. The separate processing of the check symbols can be described as a general error detection circuit, such that

$$X = X_1 \times X_2, \quad F(f) = \{f_0 = f, f_1, f_2, \ldots\} \text{ where } \exists x \in X/c(f_i(x)) \neq c(f(x))$$

and

$$\phi(x_1, x_2, y) = \begin{cases} 0 & \text{for } g(a(x_1), b(x_2)) - c(y) = 0 \\ 1 & \text{for } g(a(x_1), b(x_2)) - c(y) \neq 0 \end{cases} \tag{2.4}$$

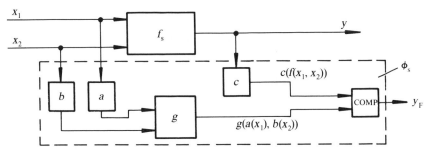

Figure 2.4 Separate processing of check symbols.

Since the circuit is completely defined by Eq. (2.4), there are no don't-care conditions.

Error detection by systematic codes is shown in Fig. 2.5. The input set $X \subseteq X$ of f is defined by the set of code words. The function f maps code words in X into code words in $Y \subseteq Y$. The checking device finds out whether $f(x)$ is a code word in Y. Thus in the special case of a binary coded decimal (BCD) code only 10 of the 16 possible four-digit binary words are code words. The checking device finds out whether the number in question is a decimal number. For $X = \{0, 1\}^n$, $Y = \{0, 1\}^m$, X and Y may, for instance, also be code words of a Hamming code.

For error detection by codes one has

$$Y = \bigcup_{x \in X} f(x), \qquad F(f) = \{f, f_1, f_2, \ldots\}$$

Here the functions f_i are those functions $f_i: X \to Y$ for which there exists an $x^* \in X$ such that $f_i(x^*) \notin Y$. The error detection function ϕ is determined by

$$\phi(x, y) = \begin{cases} 0 & \text{for } x \in X \text{ and } y \in Y \\ 1 & \text{for } x \in X \text{ and } y \notin Y \\ - & \text{otherwise} \end{cases} \qquad (2.5)$$

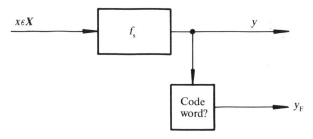

Figure 2.5 Error detection by codes.

where, however, $\phi(x, y)$ is almost always implemented in the form

$$\phi(x, y) = \begin{cases} 0 & \text{for } y \in Y \\ 1 & \text{for } y \notin Y \end{cases} \tag{2.6}$$

Equation (2.6) is obtained by fixing the don't-care conditions in Eq. (2.5) to 0 for $x \in X \backslash X$ and $y \in Y$ and to 1 for $x \in X \backslash X$ and $y \notin Y$.

2.2 EXAMPLES: ERROR DETECTION CIRCUITS FOR ADDERS

We shall now apply the method presented in the first chapter for the design of error detection circuits to different types of adders with different failure mode assumptions. Adders are very frequently used combinational circuits. There is a great variety of implementations, but the design of an error detection circuit is not without problems. An adder circuit implements a relatively complex combination of the input variables.

If the operands A and B and the sum vector of the full adder shown in Fig. 2.6 are expressed as

$$A = (a_m, a_{m-1}, \ldots, a_1, a_0)$$

$$B = (b_m, b_{m-1}, \ldots, b_1, b_0)$$

$$S = (s_m, s_{m-1}, \ldots, s_1, s_0)$$

then the ith sum bit s_i depends on $a_i, a_{i-1}, \ldots, a_1, a_0, b_i, b_{i-1}, \ldots, b_1, b_0$ and on the carry-in c_-. If the adder is implemented with minimum expenditure as a ripple adder, there is a high probability that single faults within the circuit will affect several outputs at any time. If an error detection circuit is to detect all such situations, it must be quite efficient. This generally requires a high implementation expenditure. For the adder, the various hitherto known error detection circuits almost double the size of the full circuit. Therefore,

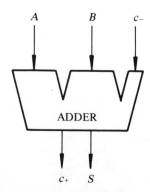

Figure 2.6 Binary adder.

optimization of error detection circuits towards only technically relevant failures is very important. In what follows we shall refer to relevant error models to show how error detection circuits for adders can be optimized and how this depends upon the error model under consideration.

To begin with, let us consider error detection for a one-digit binary adder. The 1-digit binary adder, also called an adder bit slice, represents the elementary cell from which, taking into account technical boundary conditions, adders of a great variety of word sizes can be produced by circuit cascading. Here the adder bit slice has the block structure shown in Fig. 2.6, with $A, B, c_-, c_+, S \in \{0, 1\}$. The output signals c_+ and S are derived from input signals A, B and c_- according to

$$S = S(A, B, c_-) = A \oplus B \oplus c_-$$

$$c_+ = c_+(A, B, c_-) = A \wedge B \vee A \wedge c_- \vee B \wedge c_-$$

Figure 2.7 shows a possible technical implementation of the adder bit slice using OR and NOR gates with a maximum of three inputs. The gate outputs are open-collector, providing an AND function (wired AND).

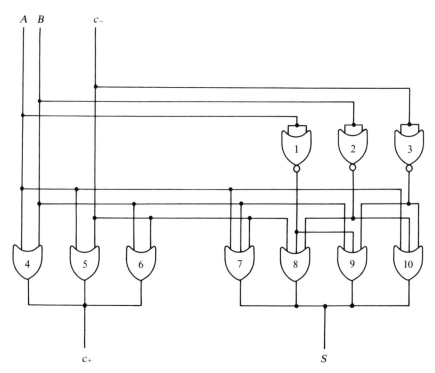

Figure 2.7 Special implementation of an adder with independent outputs.

To begin with, the demand we make upon the error detection circuit is that it detects all single faults of the gates. The analysis of Fig. 2.7 shows that single gate faults always affect, at most, one of the two output signals. Stuck-at-0 and stuck-at-1 faults of the two outputs must be taken into account. These faults can be described by the error model $F_1(f_A)$:

$$F_1(f_A) = \{f_{A10}, f_{A11}, f_{A12}, f_{A13}, f_{A14}\}$$

Here $f_{A1i} = (S_i, c_{+i})$, $i = 1, 2, 3, 4$, with

$$S_0 = A \oplus B \oplus c_-, c_{+0} = (A \wedge B) \vee (A \wedge c_-) \vee (B \wedge c_-)$$

$$S_1 = S_0, c_{+1} = 0$$

$$S_2 = S_0, c_{+2} = 1$$

$$S_3 = 0, c_{+3} = c_{+0}$$

$$S_4 = 1, c_{+4} = c_{+0}$$

The tables of values for $f_{A10}, \ldots, f_{A14}$ are summarized in Table 2.4. The input set is not restricted, and A, B, c_- can each assume the values zero and one.

For this simple error model the resulting table of values for the error detection function ϕ_{A1} shown in Table 2.5 contains don't-care conditions at exactly those points where $S_i \neq S_0$ and $c_{+i} \neq c_{+0}$. For every other additional fault of a single gate this previously derived table of values for the error detection function ϕ_{A1} remains unchanged. This is explained below. For the correct values of S and c_+ the error detection function $\phi_{A1}(A, B, c_-, S, c_+)$ is zero. If only one of the outputs of the adder is erroneous the error detection function $\phi_{A1}(A, B, c_-, S, c_+)$ according to Table 2.5 is already one and no additional one has to be added for a fault changing one output only. Since none of the gates can simultaneously influence both outputs S and c_+, the don't-care conditions located in Table 2.5 at positions where both S and c_+ are erroneous together also remain unchanged.

Thus the error detection function ϕ_{A1}, which is only designed for the

Table 2.4

A	B	c_-	S_0	c_{+0}	S_1	c_{+1}	S_2	c_{+2}	S_3	c_{+3}	S_4	c_{+4}
0	0	0	0	0	0	0	0	1	0	0	1	0
0	0	1	1	0	1	0	1	1	0	0	1	0
0	1	0	1	0	1	0	1	1	0	0	1	0
0	1	1	0	1	0	0	0	1	0	1	1	1
1	0	0	1	0	1	0	1	1	0	0	1	0
1	0	1	0	1	0	0	0	1	0	1	1	1
1	1	0	0	1	0	0	0	1	0	1	1	1
1	1	1	1	1	1	0	1	1	0	1	1	1

Table 2.5

A	B	c_-	c_+	S	ϕ_{A1}	ϕ_{A2}	ϕ_{A3}	ϕ_{A4}
0	0	0	0	0	0	0	0	0
0	0	0	0	1	1	—	—	—
0	0	0	1	0	1	—	—	—
0	0	0	1	1	—	—	—	—
0	0	1	0	0	1	1	1	—
0	0	1	0	1	0	0	0	0
0	0	1	1	0	—	—	—	—
0	0	1	1	1	1	—	—	—
0	1	0	0	0	1	1	1	—
0	1	0	0	1	0	0	0	0
0	1	0	1	0	—	—	—	—
0	1	0	1	1	1	—	—	—
0	1	1	0	0	1	1	—	—
0	1	1	0	1	—	—	—	—
0	1	1	1	0	0	0	0	0
0	1	1	1	1	1	—	1	1
1	0	0	0	0	1	1	1	—
1	0	0	0	1	0	0	0	0
1	0	0	1	0	—	—	—	—
1	0	0	1	1	1	—	—	—
1	0	1	0	0	1	1	—	—
1	0	1	0	1	—	—	—	—
1	0	1	1	0	0	0	0	0
1	0	1	1	1	1	—	1	1
1	1	0	0	0	1	1	—	—
1	1	0	0	1	—	—	—	—
1	1	0	1	0	0	0	0	0
1	1	0	1	1	1	—	1	1
1	1	1	0	0	—	—	—	—
1	1	1	0	1	1	1	—	—
1	1	1	1	0	1	1	—	—
1	1	1	1	1	0	0	0	0

detection of single stuck-at-0/1 faults of the circuit of Fig. 2.7, detects all single gate faults (if they result for the first time in an erroneous output). As a possible solution one obtains

$$\phi_{A1}(A, B, c_-, c_+, S) = ((A \vee B \vee c_-) \wedge (A \vee B \vee c_-)) \oplus S \oplus c_+$$

If this function is now implemented with the same components as those used to build up the circuit to be monitored, then 12 gates are required (Fig. 2.8). This corresponds to an increase in hardware by more than 100 per cent, compared to the circuit without error detection.

To evaluate the increase, all gates on a component basis are regarded as equivalent, so that their number represents a measure of the hardware

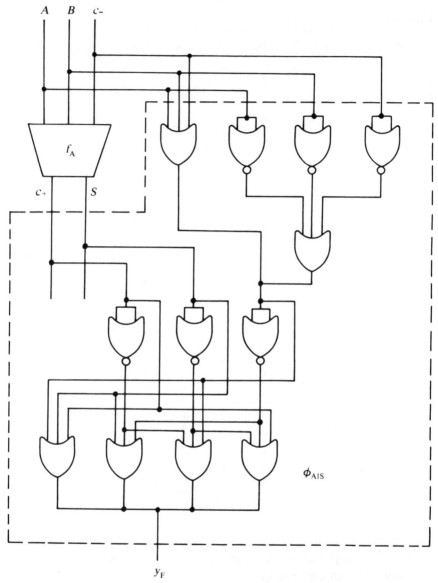

Figure 2.8 Error detection circuit for an adder detecting all single gate failures.

expenditure. Nevertheless, the expenditure for this error detection circuit is less than that required for duplicating the original circuit, followed by a comparison of the output signals. In this case 21 gates of the assumed OR/NOR basis would be required.

We now discuss the same 1-bit adder of Fig. 2.7 and suppose that the faults of the OR/NOR gates are shortages to ground of their outputs. The error models of the components are

$$F(G_{\text{OR}}) = \{G_{\text{OR0}} = x_1 \vee x_2 \vee x_3, G_{\text{OR1}} = 0\}$$

$$F(G_{\text{NOR}}) = \{G_{\text{NOR0}} = \overline{x_1 \vee x_2 \vee x_3}, G_{\text{NOR1}} = 0\}$$

Further, we again assume that at most one component in the circuit of Fig. 2.7 is faulty.

If the outputs of the ith gate, $i = 1, \ldots, 10$, in the circuit of Fig. 2.7 are fixed to zero (stuck-at-0 faults) one after the other, then an analysis of the circuit gives the tables of values of the functions $f_{\text{A}2i} = (S_i, c_{+i})$ of Table 2.6, which together with the standard function $f_{\text{A}20} = (S_0, c_{+0})$ form the error model $F_2(f_\text{A}) = \{f_{\text{A}20}, f_{\text{A}21}, \ldots, f_{\text{A}210}\}$.

Using definition (2.1) this gives the error-detecting function $\phi_{\text{A}2}$ of Table 2.5. This function can, for instance, be represented by the expression

$$\phi_{\text{A}2}(A, B, c_-, c_+, S) = \overline{(c_+ \vee S)} \wedge (A \vee B \vee c_-) \vee A \wedge (\overline{B} \vee c_+) \wedge (\overline{B} \vee c_- \vee S)$$

Figure 2.9 shows the corresponding error detection circuit. It is made up of nine gates. This corresponds to an increase of 90 per cent, compared to the case without an error detection circuit. According to the error model used, the error detection circuit has the property that it indicates any stuck-at-0 faults of a gate output at the time of its first effect on the output of the adder bit slice.

Basically, the probabilities for different types of components to be faulty are different. Thus certain components on a component basis may fail much more frequently than others. Consider the case where, among the components of the OR and the NOR type, those of the NOR type fail very frequently while the failures of the OR gates are so improbable that they can be neglected.

Let the error model of the NOR gates be given by

$$F'(G_{\text{NOR}}) = \{G_{\text{NOR0}} = \overline{x_1 \vee x_2 \vee x_3}, G_{\text{NOR1}} = x_1 \vee x_2 \vee x_3\}$$

This means that the NOR gates used act as OR gates if internal component faults occur. Moreover, we again assume that at most one NOR gate is faulty at a time. Replacing (in Fig. 2.7) the NOR gates 1, 2, 3 one after the other by OR gates and analysing the behaviour of the circuits resulting in this way, we obtain the tables of values (see Table 2.7) for the functions $f_{\text{A}3i} = (S_i, c_{+i})$, $i = 1, 2, 3$. Together with the standard function $f_{\text{A}30} = (S_0, c_{+0})$, these functions form the error model $F_3(f_\text{A}) = \{f_{\text{A}30}, f_{\text{A}31}, f_{\text{A}32}, f_{\text{A}33}\}$. For the error-detecting function $\phi_{\text{A}3}$ in Table 2.5 one has

$$\phi_{\text{A}3}(A, B, c_-, c_+, S) = (\overline{S} \vee c_+) \wedge (S \vee \overline{c}_+) \wedge (A \vee B \vee c_-) \wedge (\overline{A} \vee \overline{B} \vee \overline{c}_-)$$

The technical implementation of this function, which is shown in Fig. 2.10, also consists of nine gates.

If the NOR gates of the adder bit slice of Fig. 2.7 are implemented in a circuit and if, as a result of a concrete technological failure, the error of a

Table 2.6

A	B	c_-	S_0	c_{+0}	S_1	c_{+1}	S_2	c_{+2}	S_3	c_{+3}	S_4	c_{+4}	S_5	c_{+5}
0	0	0	0	0	0	0	0	0	0	0	0	0	0	0
0	0	1	1	0	0	0	0	0	1	0	1	0	1	0
0	1	0	0	0	0	0	1	0	0	0	1	0	1	0
0	1	1	1	1	0	1	0	1	0	1	0	0	0	0
1	0	0	0	0	1	0	0	0	0	0	1	0	1	0
1	0	1	0	1	0	1	0	1	0	1	0	0	0	0
1	1	0	0	1	0	1	0	1	0	1	0	0	0	0
1	1	1	1	1	1	1	1	1	1	1	1	0	1	0

A	B	c_-	S_6	c_{+6}	S_7	c_{+7}	S_8	c_{+8}	S_9	c_{+9}	S_{10}	c_{+10}
0	0	0	0	0	0	0	0	0	0	0	0	0
0	0	1	1	0	0	0	0	0	0	0	0	0
0	1	0	0	0	0	0	0	0	0	0	0	0
0	1	1	1	0	0	1	0	1	0	1	0	1
1	0	0	0	0	0	0	0	0	0	0	0	0
1	0	1	0	0	0	1	0	1	0	1	0	1
1	1	0	0	0	0	1	0	1	0	1	0	1
1	1	1	1	0	0	1	0	1	0	1	0	1

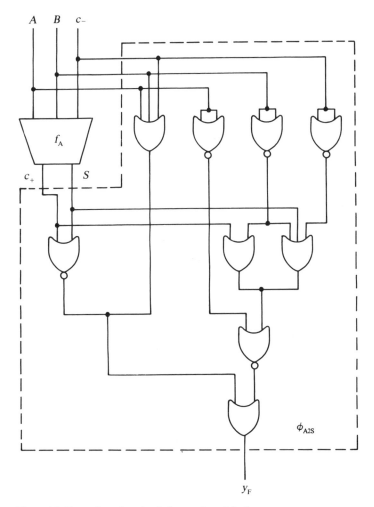

Figure 2.9 Error detection circuit for stuck-at-0 faults.

NOR-to-OR gate conversion occurs either in all three NOR gates simultaneously or does not occur at all, then the corresponding error model is $F_4(f_A) = \{f_{A40}, f_{A41}\}$, with $f_{A4i} = \{S_i, c_{+i}\}$ for $i = 0, 1$.

In the model, only the error function f_{A41} is then left, which is obtained by replacing the NOR gates 1, 2, 3 in Fig. 2.7 by OR gates all at the same time and analysing the behaviour of the resulting circuit. The functions f_{A40} and f_{A41} are shown as tables of values in Table 2.8.

The table of values for the error-detecting function ϕ_{A4} (Table 2.5), which can be determined from Table 2.8, can be represented by the formula

$$\phi_{A4}(A, B, c_-, c_+, S) = S \wedge c_+ \wedge (\bar{A} \vee \bar{B} \vee \bar{c}_-)$$

Table 2.7

A	B	c_-	S_0	c_{+0}	S_1	c_{+1}	S_2	c_{+2}	S_3	c_{+3}
0	0	0	0	0	0	0	0	0	0	0
0	0	1	1	0	0	0	0	0	1	0
0	1	0	1	0	0	0	1	0	0	0
0	1	1	0	1	0	1	1	1	1	1
1	0	0	1	0	1	0	0	0	0	0
1	0	1	0	1	1	1	0	1	1	1
1	1	0	0	1	1	1	1	1	0	1
1	1	1	1	1	1	1	1	1	1	1

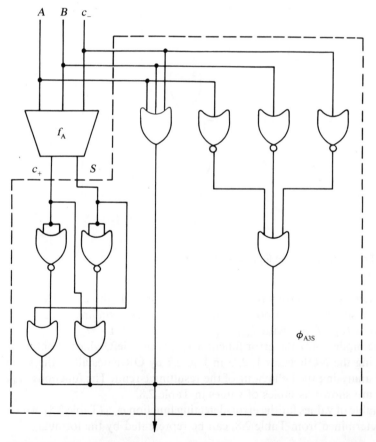

Figure 2.10 Error detection circuit for a special fault model explained in the text.

Table 2.8

A	B	c_-	S_0	c_{+0}	S_1	c_{+1}
0	0	0	0	0	0	0
0	0	1	1	0	1	0
0	1	0	1	0	1	0
0	1	1	0	1	1	1
1	0	0	1	0	1	0
1	0	1	0	1	1	1
1	1	0	0	1	1	1
1	1	1	1	1	1	1

Fig. 2.11 shows a possible technical implementation of ϕ_{A4} consisting of six gates. The hardware overhead is then 60 per cent.

From the error detection circuits derived so far for the adder bit slice, an error detection circuit for an $(m + 1)$-bit adder can be derived in a simple way, as shown in Fig. 2.12. Here it is assumed for the present that all intermediate carries between the bit slices are available.

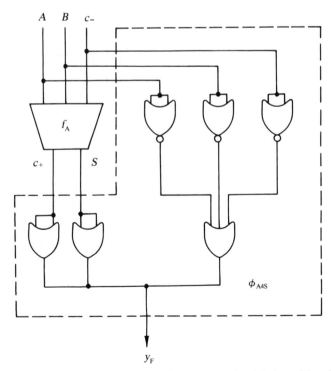

Figure 2.11 Error detection circuit for a very restricted fault model explained in the text.

For the error detection circuit ϕ_A^i, $i = 0, 1, \ldots, m$, of the individual bit slices it is possible to use, among other things, all the previous solutions. If the individual bit slices are based on standardized technical parameters, especially on a standardized component basis, then

$$\phi_A^0 = \phi_A^1 = \cdots = \phi_A^i$$

An error detection circuit for bit slices of larger compositions is arrived at via partial solutions and is practicable whenever the input and output signals of all the component circuits considered are available. However, if, for example, an error detection circuit for a four-bit adder ($m = 3$) is to be designed, where the circuit to be monitored is integrated in a medium-scale integrated (MSI) circuit and the intermediate carries c_0, c_1 and c_2 are not available at the edge of the integrated circuit (IC), then the desired error detection circuit cannot easily be composed of the existing solutions for the bit slice. Additional regeneration of the missing signals causes an additional overhead in hardware. If this cannot be accepted for economic reasons, then one has no choice but to design an error detection circuit for the whole four-bit adder.

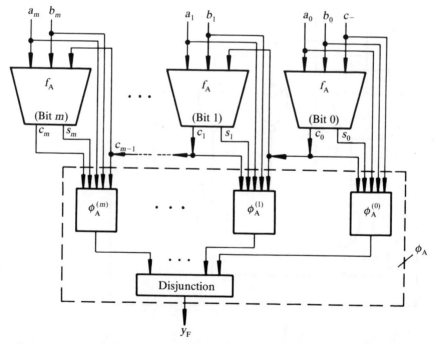

Figure 2.12 Error detection circuit for an n-bit adder derived from error detection circuits for 1-bit adders.

Generally, the derivation of an overall solution for a composite circuit leads to lower hardware expenditure than when assembling component circuits. Problems arise when dealing with a complex design problem, for the designer needs to decompose more complex circuits into partial circuits that can be mastered by an individual designer. The question of how to solve the structuring problem of a circuit for each particular case can be decided only by consideration of all the boundary conditions of the actual application.

The computer aided design of complex combinational and sequential circuits will be dealt with in Chapter 4.

2.3 ERROR DETECTION FOR ARBITRARY SINGLE ERRORS (method according to Sogomonyan)

In this section we describe a method developed by Sogomonyan (1970), which, for a combinational circuit f_s, designed to implement a function f: $\{0, 1\}^n \to \{0, 1\}^m$; $n, m > 0$, shows how an error model $F(f)$ is determined in such a way that the error detection circuit ϕ_s detects at least all possible single errors. The error model also contains as few functions as possible.

This method also attempts to reduce the overhead required to establish the functional error model of the circuit. However, as already pointed out, it is suitable only for the specific task of detecting all the single errors of a combinational circuit, and thus still leads to relatively expensive error detection circuits.

In this method, the maximal classes of elements of a circuit with one output for each maximal class are determined. The elements are the gates and the outputs of the circuit considered. All faults concerning an arbitrary single gate can be modelled in the following way. The outputs of every maximal class are replaced, one after the other, by their negated outputs. The respective functions implemented by the combinational circuit are the functions of the error model. The negation of the outputs of the maximal classes are single faults. Therefore, they should be included in the set of faults in order to determine the functional error model. For all negated values of the outputs of the maximal classes that change the outputs of the circuit, the corresponding error detection function has to be one. Every additional fault of a specific element affecting the behaviour of the circuit has to change the output of its class for some inputs to its opposite value. For such erroneous values, however, by changing the output of the circuit the error detection function of the circuit has already been determined to be one. The error will be automatically detected if the error model contains all of the functions described above.

The error model $F(f)$ contains as many functions $f_1, f_2, \ldots$ as there are different maximal classes with one output. If the combinational circuit only has one output, then the method naturally leads to duplication and comparison. The advantage of the method lies in the small set of functions of the error model, which concern a fairly extensive set of errors, namely all errors concerning only elements of one class, and hence also all possible single errors.

A disadvantage is that this approach is not suitable for other, more specific or weakened fault assumptions, as discussed in the previous section. In Sec. 2.4 these requirements will be dealt with for errors concerning certain spatial regions of the chip, which do not necessarily contain only elements of a single class. The maximal classes and the elements with the outputs of these classes, called the smallest elements of these classes, are determined according to the following rule. The components of the combinational circuit considered are numbered from 1 through m. In a table of connections of the components and outputs, with m rows and $m + 1$ columns, a one is entered into the place (i, j) if in the circuit f_s there is a direct connection leading from component B_i to component B_j, $i \neq j$. If the component B_k is directly connected with an output of the circuit, then a one is entered into the place $(k, m + 1)$, with $1 \leqslant i, j, k \leqslant m$.

The actual method of determining the classes K_B and their smallest elements consists of the following six steps:

1. Mark a row of the table by ** in which a one occurs only in the $(m + 1)$th column. (Such a row exists, because f_s does not contain any feedback.)
2. Mark the column with the number equal to that of the row just marked by *.
3. Find a row that has ones entered only in marked columns. If such a row exists, then mark it by * and proceed to step 2; otherwise proceed to step 4.
4. Delete the marked rows and columns from the table. (The components with the numbers of the deleted rows form a class K_B. The component with the number of the row marked by ** is the smallest.)
5. If a one in a non-marked row is deleted when deleting a column, then add a one in the $(m + 1)$th column of this row.
6. If there are still non-deleted rows, then return to step 1. If all rows of the table are deleted, then the procedure is finished.

To begin with, let us explain Sogomonyan's method by again considering the adder bit slice shown in Fig. 2.7, which consists of open-collector OR and NOR elements with at most three inputs. Since in the method, as a matter of principle, a circuit is interpreted as a set of interconnected components, the open-collector outputs of the gates 4, 5, 6 and 7, 8, 9 and 10, which functionally create an AND gate, must be replaced by the AND gates 11 and 12. Thus the circuit of Fig. 2.7 gives the equivalent circuit shown in Fig. 2.13. The components of this circuit are numbered from 1 to 12. Hence Table 2.9, showing the connections of the components and outputs of the circuit, consists of 12 rows and 13 columns. It contains a one in the

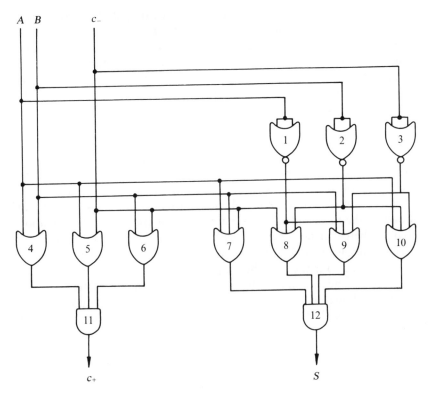

Figure 2.13 Circuit functionally equivalent to the circuit of Fig. 2.7.

Table 2.9

	1	2	3	*4	*5	*6	7	8	9	10	*11	12	13
1								1	1				
2								1		1			
3									1	1			
4											1		*
5											1		*
6											1		*
7												1	
8												1	
9												1	
10											1		
11												1	**
12												1	

place (i, j) $(i =$ row index, $j =$ column index) if the output of the component i is connected with the input of the component j; it contains a one in the place $(i, 13)$ if the output of the component i is connected with an output of the circuit. Here one has $i, j \in \{1, 2, \ldots, 12\}$. Thus, for instance, the output of component 1 is connected with an input of the components 8 and 9, and therefore a one is entered into each of the places $(1, 8)$ and $(1, 9)$ of Table 2.9. A one also occurs in the place $(11, 13)$, since component 11 is connected with an output.

We select row 11 as the first row containing a one only in column 13. It is marked by ** (step 1 of the procedure). Now column 11 is marked by * (step 2). It contains ones in the rows 4, 5 and 6. Row 4 satisfies the requirements of step 3 because it does not contain any entries except in the marked column 11. We mark row 4, and hence also column 4, by *. This is followed by the rows and columns 5 and 6, which also satisfy the conditions of step 3. Thereafter no other row with this property is encountered.

The components 4, 5, 6 and 11 form the class $K_{B1} = \{4, 5, 6, \underline{11}\}$, where 11 is underlined to mark it as the output element of K_{B1}. After deleting the marked rows and columns (step 4) we obtain the remaining table of connections shown in Table 2.10. Using this table, the procedure described above is repeated. We mark row 12 by **, because it contains a one only in column 13. Then column 12 is marked by *. One may proceed with any of the rows 7, 8, 9 or 10, all of which have only one entry in the marked column 12. We mark row 7 and column 7. Since column 7 does not contain any ones, there is no new situation. Therefore we proceed to mark row 8 and column 8. The latter contains entries in the rows 1 and 2. These two rows, however, contain further ones in the hitherto unmarked columns 9 and 10, respectively, which means that they do not satisfy the conditions of step 3. Therefore we continue the procedure by marking row 9 and column

Table 2.10

	*	*	*	*	*	*	*	*	*
	1	2	3	7	8	9	10	12	13
1					1	1			*
2					1		1		*
3						1	1		*
7								1	*
8								1	*
9								1	*
10								1	*
12									1 **

9. This is followed by 1, 10, 2, 3, in this order of succession, if the search process for marked rows always starts with the lowest index. Now all of the rows of Table 2.10 are marked, and the components 1, 2, 3, 7, 8, 9, 10 and 12 form a class K_{B2} with the output element 12, $K_{B2} = \{1, 2, 3, 7, 8, 9, 10, \underline{12}\}$. This completes the procedure of classification.

The functions f'_{A1} and f'_{A2} of the error model $F'(f_A)$ for the detection of all single faults are determined by replacing each of the smallest elements 11 and 12 of the classes K_{B1} and K_{B2} by their negated elements. In the case considered this corresponds to a negation of the carry output and sum output, respectively, of the adder bit slice, so that

$$f'_{Aj} = (S'_j, c'_{+j}), \qquad j = 0, 1, 2$$

with $S'_0 = S_0$, $S'_1 = \bar{S}_0$, $S'_2 = S_0$, $c'_{+0} = c_{+0}$, $c'_{+1} = c_{+0}$, $c'_{+2} = \bar{c}_{+0}$ and

$$F'(f_A) = \{f'_{A0}, f'_{A1}, f'_{A2}\}$$

The tables of values for the functions of the error model $F'(f_A)$ are summarized in Table 2.11.

The resulting table of values for the error detection function ϕ'_A of Table 2.12 is identical with the function ϕ_{A1} shown in Table 2.5 of Sec. 2.2, which had been determined with the assumption of single stuck-at-0/1 failures for each circuit output. Implementation of this function has already been shown in Fig. 2.8.

As a second example, where the procedure described above leads to duplication and comparison in spite of the required restricted error detection properties, let us consider the implementation of the adder bit slice from NAND gates with two inputs, as shown in Fig. 2.14. The gates are numbered from 1 to 14, and the table of connections of the components and outputs, given in Table 2.13, has 14 rows and 15 columns.

Table 2.11

A	B	c_-	S'_0	c'_{+0}	S'_1	c'_{+1}	S'_2	c'_{+2}
0	0	0	0	0	0	1	1	0
0	0	1	1	0	1	1	0	0
0	1	0	1	0	1	1	0	0
0	1	1	0	1	0	0	1	1
1	0	0	1	0	1	1	0	0
1	0	1	0	1	0	0	1	1
1	1	0	0	1	0	0	1	1
1	1	1	1	1	1	0	0	1

Table 2.12

A	B	c_-	S	c_+	ϕ'_A	ϕ''_A	A	B	c_-	S	c_+	ϕ'_A	ϕ''_A
0	0	0	0	0	0	0	0	0	0	1	0	1	1
0	0	1	1	0	0	0	0	0	1	0	0	1	1
0	1	0	1	0	0	0	0	1	0	0	0	1	1
0	1	1	0	1	0	0	0	1	1	1	1	1	1
1	0	0	1	0	0	0	1	0	0	0	0	1	1
1	0	1	0	1	0	0	1	0	1	1	1	1	1
1	1	0	0	1	0	0	1	1	0	1	1	1	1
1	1	1	1	1	0	1	1	1	1	0	1	1	1
0	0	0	0	1	1	1	0	0	0	1	1	−	−
0	0	1	1	1	1	1	0	0	1	0	1	−	−
0	1	0	1	1	1	1	0	1	0	0	0	−	−
0	1	1	0	0	1	1	0	1	1	1	1	−	1
1	0	0	1	1	1	1	1	0	0	0	0	−	1
1	0	1	0	0	1	1	1	0	1	1	0	−	−
1	1	0	0	0	1	1	1	1	0	0	0	−	1
1	1	1	1	0	1	1	1	1	1	1	0	−	−

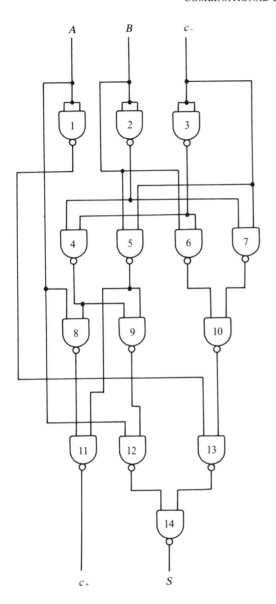

Figure 2.14 Implementation of an adder by NAND gates.

Table 2.13

	1	2	3	4	5	6	7	8	9	10	11	12	13	14	15
1													1		
2				1			1								
3				1		1									
4								1	1						
5									1		1				
6										1					
7										1					
8											1				
9												1			
10													1		
11															1
12														1	
13														1	
14															1

Following the algorithm described previously, we obtain the classes of components, with underlined smallest components:

$$K_{B1} = \{8, \underline{11}\}$$
$$K_{B2} = \{1, 2, 7, 9, 10, 12, 13, \underline{14}\}$$
$$K_{B3} = \{\underline{4}\}$$
$$K_{B4} = \{\underline{2}\}$$
$$K_{B5} = \{\underline{3}\}$$
$$K_{B6} = \{\underline{5}\}$$

and apart from the standard function $f''_{A0} = (S''_0, c''_{+0}) = f_A = (S_0, c_{+0})$, the error model $F''(f_A)$ consists of the six functions $f''_{Ai} = (S''_i, c''_{+i})$, $i = 1, \ldots, 6$, where the functions f''_{Ai} are determined from the circuit of Fig. 2.14 by replacing the smallest component of the class K_{Bi} by the corresponding negated component. (Consequently, the NAND gates 11, 14, 4, 2, 3, 5 have to be replaced by AND gates.) The tables of values for the functions f''_{A0}, $f''_{A1}, \ldots, f''_{A6}$ are shown in Table 2.14. The error-detecting function ϕ''_A shown in Table 2.12 is again determined from Table 2.14.

In contrast to the circuit shown in Fig. 2.13, there are smallest components that functionally affect both of the outputs of the adder bit slice. If these components are replaced by the corresponding negated components, this may cause differences in the behaviour of the two outputs.

The function ϕ''_A exhibits only five don't-care conditions. Owing to the small number of degrees of freedom for the optimization, we did not find a

Table 2.14

A	B	c_-	S_0	c_0	S_1	c_{+1}	S_2	c_{+2}	S_3	c_{+3}	S_4	c_{+4}	S_5	c_{+5}	S_6	c_{+6}
0	0	0	0	0	0	1	1	0	0	0	0	0	0	0	0	1
0	0	1	1	0	1	1	0	0	1	0	0	0	1	0	1	1
0	1	0	1	0	1	1	0	0	1	0	1	0	0	0	1	1
0	1	1	0	1	0	0	1	1	0	1	0	1	1	1	0	0
1	0	0	1	0	1	1	0	0	0	1	0	1	1	1	1	1
1	0	1	0	1	0	0	1	1	1	0	1	1	0	0	1	1
1	1	0	0	1	0	0	1	1	1	0	1	0	1	1	1	1
1	1	1	1	1	1	0	0	1	1	1	1	1	1	1	0	1

hardware implementation of the function ϕ''_A whose overhead would be less than that required for duplicating the adder circuit with a subsequent bit-wise comparison of the outputs. Here, as usual, the error detection circuit was assumed to have the same component basis as the circuit to be monitored (NAND gates with a maximum of two inputs).

2.4 REDUCED ERROR DETECTION

In the preceding sections of this chapter we have described, for a combinational circuit with a known error model, how to determine an optimum error detection circuit. This detects every error of the error model at the time of its first effect on the behaviour of the circuit. We shall now investigate the question of whether and how the overhead for error detection can be further reduced in a reasonable way. If, for instance, a circuit is designed on a gate array in such a way that a certain number of gates remains unused, then the question to be asked is how these gates can reasonably be utilized for error detection.

When designing a computer, it must be made clear how, given a limited expenditure to be paid for error detection, as many errors as possible can be detected in the periods between two maintenance times. Since the method described in the first section warrants an optimum size of error detection circuit, which detects every error of the error model upon its first effect on the behaviour of the circuit, the matter to be discussed here can only be a modification of the original problem.

To begin with, it is reasonable to reduce the overhead required for error detection by restricting the error model by, for example, taking into account only one half, a quarter, an eighth, etc., of all errors when determining the error detection circuit. This approach in principle does not require any new considerations. Another interesting possibility of reducing the overhead now consists in demanding that errors of the circuit to be monitored need to be detected only if certain bit patterns are applied. For other bit patterns this results in additional don't-care conditions for the error-detecting function, which can be utilized for optimization purposes. If, at any time, a (permanent) error occurs for the first time, then it will not be detected until a suitable bit pattern is applied to the input lines of the circuit.

The average time that elapses between the first effect of an error and its detection by the error detection circuit is called the average error latency period. It is clear that the average error latency period must be much shorter than the maintenance interval of the system, so an error detection circuit can be useful. In order to formulate weakening requirements on error detection more precisely, we assign to each function $f_i \in F(f)$ a set $X_i \subseteq X$, $X_i \neq \emptyset$, such that

$$x \in X_i \text{ implies that } f_i(x) \neq f(x)$$

Generally X_i is a subset of those inputs for which f_i and f are different. We define the weakened error detection function $\phi_a(x, y)$ by

$$\phi_a(x, y) =$$

$$\begin{cases} 0 & \text{for } x \in X \text{ and } y = f(x) \\ 1 & \text{for } \exists f_i \in F(f) \text{ with } x \in X_i \text{ and } y = f_i(x) \neq f(x) \quad (2.7) \\ -(\text{don't care}) & \text{otherwise} \end{cases}$$

If f is erroneous in f_i, then this error is detected with certainty when an input x in X_i is submitted. For $x \in X \backslash X_i$ and $f(x) \neq f_i(x)$ the weakened error detection function $\phi_a(x, y)$ is not defined for the present. Depending on whether $\phi_a(x, y)$ is assigned the value one or zero during optimization, this error is detected, or not, by the corresponding circuit.

To be able to perform reduced error detection using existing computer programs, it is reasonable to use off-line test sets. For simple component failures, test sets for combinational circuits are generally determined by computer programs. Therefore it is very desirable for reduced on-line error detection circuits to be derived immediately from the computer-determined off-line test sets.

Here a set $\tilde{X}$ is called a complete off-line test set for a combinational circuit f_s for an error model $F(f_s)$ if for every function $f_i \in F(f)$ there exists at least one $x_i \in \tilde{X}$ such that $f(x_i) \neq f_i(x_i)$. Starting from an off-line test set $\tilde{X}$, the weakened error detection function $\phi_a(x, y)$ is required to satisfy

$$\phi_a(x, y) = \begin{cases} 0 & \text{for } x \in \tilde{X} \text{ and } y = f(x) \\ 1 & \text{for } x \in \tilde{X} \text{ and } y \neq f(x) \quad (2.8) \\ -(\text{don't care}) & \text{otherwise} \end{cases}$$

For the same circuit and the same error model, Eq. (2.8) exhibits less don't-care conditions than Eq. (2.7). However, Eq. (2.8) has the advantage that $\phi_a(x, y)$ can be determined immediately from the automatically evaluated test set without having further reference to the individual functions of the error model.

For a first example of reduced error detection and the associated saving effect, let us again consider the adder bit slice of Fig. 2.7 with a stuck-at-0 error model $F_2(f_A) = \{f_{A0}, f_{A1}, \ldots, f_{A10}\}$ and the 11 functions $f_{Ai} = (S_i, c_{+i})$, $i = 0, \ldots, 10$, shown in Table 2.6. Proceeding on the assumption that each of the eight possible input bit patterns occurs frequently enough and assuming that the inputs change rapidly because of high-frequency use of the adder, we start from the fact that it will suffice to detect each of the ten erroneous functions of the error model as being erroneous for at least one bit pattern. Because the adder is used frequently, this pattern is likely to occur. For those subsets of the inputs X_{2i} for which the error 'f_{A0} changed into f_{Ai}' is to be detected with certainty by the error detection circuit, we set $X_{21} = X_{27} =$

$X_{28} = X_{29} = X_{210} = \{001, 010\}$, $X_{22} = \{001\}$, $X_{23} = \{010\}$, $X_{24} = X_{25} = X_{26} = \{011\}$.

The table of values for the weakened error detection function $\phi_{aA2}(x, y)$ according to Eq. (2.7) is shown in Table 2.15. Apart from the three input bit patterns with $\phi_{aA2} = 1$, the last column shows the error functions that are detected by these bit patterns. The bit patterns for A, B, c_-, c_+, S not listed in Table 2.15 are don't-care conditions for ϕ_{aA2}.

A possible expression for the partially defined Boolean function ϕ_{aA2} reads

$$\phi_{aA2}(A, B, c_-, c_+, S) = (A \vee B \vee c_-) \wedge \overline{(c_+ \vee S)}$$

Figure 2.15 shows an implementation of this function, which presupposes the component basis already used in Sec. 2.2. The implementation consists of only two gates. The overhead as compared with the adder circuit without error detection (Fig. 2.7) thus reduces to as little as 20 per cent.

Let us add that the set $\tilde{X} = \{001, 010, 011\}$ is an off-line test set for the error model $F_2(f_A)$. If we could determine the reduced error detection circuit from this off-line test set according to Eq. (2.8), then Table 2.15 would have to be supplemented by the six additional conditions of Table 2.16. In this case, in fact six don't-care conditions less than in the determination according to Eq. (2.7) would be available for optimization.

For larger circuits that need to be monitored frequently, very favourable solutions can be obtained, as will be explained for the example of an adder IC with a word length of 4 bits. For the operands A and B, the sum S, and the carries c one has

$$A = (a_3, \ldots, a_0)$$

$$B = (b_3, \ldots, b_0)$$

$$S = (s_3, \ldots, s_0)$$

$$c_+ = (c_3, \ldots, c_0)$$

Table 2.15

A	B	c_-	c_+	S	ϕ_{aA2}	Detected error function
0	0	0	0	0	0	—
0	0	1	0	1	0	—
0	1	0	0	1	0	—
0	1	1	1	0	0	—
1	0	0	0	1	0	—
1	0	1	1	0	0	—
1	1	0	1	0	0	—
1	1	1	1	1	0	—
0	0	1	0	0	1	$f_{A21}, f_{A22}, f_{A27}, f_{A28}, f_{A29}, f_{A210}$
0	1	0	0	0	1	$f_{A21}, f_{A23}, f_{A27}, f_{A28}, f_{A29}, f_{A210}$
0	1	1	0	0	1	$f_{A24}, f_{A25}, f_{A26}$

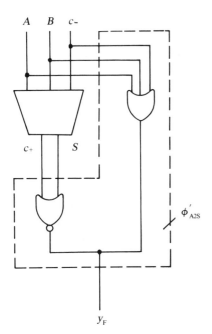

y_F

Figure 2.15 Reduced error detection circuit for stuck-at-0 faults.

Let each binary digit be implemented within the IC by a circuit according to Fig. 2.7. Accordingly, the IC contains 40 gates. The intermediate carries c_0, c_1 and c_2 are not available at the pins of the chip. The out-carry of the 4-bit adder is c_3.

As an error model we again assume one stuck-at-0 fault per gate output. For the 4-bit adder this gives an error model $F(f_{4A})$, which contains 40 error functions in addition to the standard function. It can be represented in the form $F(f_{4A}) = \{f_{4A0}, f_{4A1}, \ldots, f_{4A40}\}$. An error-detecting function is required with reduced error-detecting properties according to Eq. (2.7). The tables of

Table 2.16

A	B	c_-	c_+	S	ϕ_{aA2}
0	0	1	1	0	1
0	0	1	1	1	1
0	1	0	1	0	1
0	1	0	1	1	1
0	1	1	0	1	1
0	1	1	1	1	1

values of the 40 error functions and of the error-detecting function ϕ_{a4A} are not listed here for reasons of space.

The weakened error-detecting function ϕ_{a4A} can be described by the formula

$$\phi_{a4A}(a_3, \ldots, a_0, b_3, \ldots, b_0, c_-, c_3, s_3, \ldots, s_0) =$$

$$(a_3 \vee \cdots \vee a_0 \vee b_3 \vee \cdots \vee b_0 \vee c_-) \wedge \overline{(c_3 \vee s_3 \vee \cdots \vee s_0)}$$

Figure 2.16 shows an implementation of this function, which consists of just six gates. The overhead is thus a mere 15 per cent. Compared with the preceding example, the relative extra expenditure has been reduced by another 5 per cent, using the same error model and the same weakening condition.

Finally, let us state an example to illustrate how existing redundancy in circuitry can reasonably be utilized in the design of an error detection circuit. To this end we consider a 4m-digit binary adder, $m > 1$, which is made up

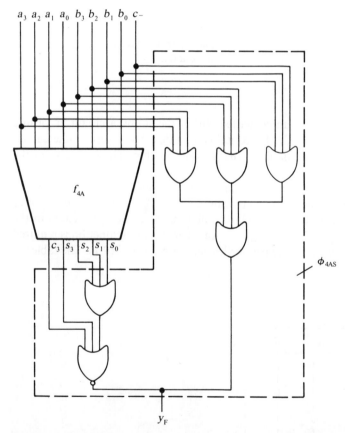

Figure 2.16 Reduced error detection circuit for a 4-bit adder for stuck-at-0 faults.

of adder bit slices according to Fig. 2.7 and in which each set of four adder bit slices is assigned a carry-look-ahead element. The most significant carry c'_4 is formed in the carry-look-ahead element by the formula

$$c'_3 = G \vee (P \wedge c_-)$$

Here P (propagated carry) means the retransmission condition for an in-carry, where c_- is the in-carry. G is the condition for the new generation of a carry in the 4-bit adder. P and G are functions of the operands of the corresponding 4-bit adder alone and can be formed in parallel. In the case of an error-free operation one has $c'_3 = c_3$.

For any error in the formation of a carry c_i, $i = 0, 1, 2, 3$, it is possible to state at least one input bit pattern of the corresponding 4-bit adder, such that the error affects its carry output. Thus, comparing c_3 and c'_3 by means of the comparator, ϕ_{SA1} is a sufficient measure of error detection for all carries within the 4-bit adder if an error latency period is acceptable.

In a further step, one still has to design an error detection circuit ϕ_{SA2} for the sum vector, where all carries can be assumed to be checked by ϕ_{SA1}.

An upper limit of overhead for ϕ_{SA2} is given by a duplication of those gates of each bit slice that contribute to the formation of the sum bit. As is easily seen from Fig. 2.7, this concerns the gates 1, 2, 3, 7, 8, 9, 10. A bit-wise comparison of the sum bits s_i, $i = 0, 1, 2, 3$, with the corresponding outputs s'_i of the duplicated circuit yields the error signal. The structure of ϕ_{SA2} for

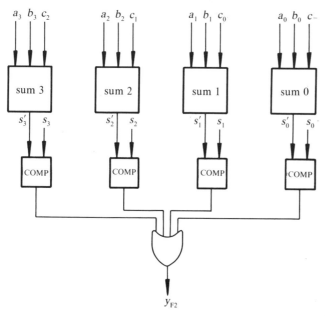

Figure 2.17 Error detection circuit for a 4-bit adder under the assumption of checked carries.

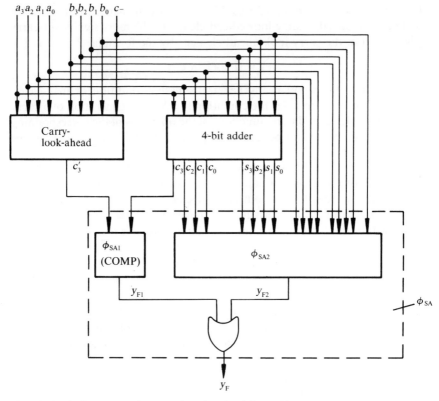

Figure 2.18 Block structure of an error detection circuit for a 4-bit adder utilizing the redundancy of the carry-look-ahead bit.

this case is shown in Fig. 2.17. Here each sum of the subcircuits i, $i = 0$, 1, 2, 3, contains the summation circuit for one binary digit according to Fig. 2.7.

Owing to the presence of ϕ_{SA1}, it is only necessary to duplicate part of the adder circuit, even without further assumptions about an error model. From the preceding examples it is clear that the hardware overhead required for ϕ_{SA2} is generally reduced if special error models are assumed for the sum section of the adder.

The block structure of the total error detection circuit for the high-speed adder is shown in Fig. 2.18.

2.5 SUMMARY

A systematic method for the design of combinational error detection circuits has been described. Starting with a functional error model corresponding to a set of technical faults, this concept was introduced for combinational circuits with the error model as a set of error functions. The systematic design of an error detection circuit was reduced to the optimal implementation of a partially defined Boolean function, the error detection function, which is a standard problem of circuit design.

The error detection circuit is designed in such a way that it detects when the monitored circuit exhibits an incorrect output, which is a possible output of at least one of the error functions in the considered error model. Other erroneous outputs must not arise, and for these outputs the error detection function remains undetermined. The resulting don't-care conditions can be used for the optimization of the error detection circuit. The error detection circuit is optimal if the CAD tool used guarantees an optimal implementation of partially defined Boolean functions.

The systematic design of a combinational error detection circuit can be performed in the following steps:

1. Determine the functional error model based on the component failures to be expected.
2. Determine the partially defined error detection function according to Eq. (2.1).
3. Optimize the error detection function by existing CAD methods.
4. Implement the optimal error detection function.

The known types of solutions, such as duplication and comparison, error detection by codes and others, were shown to be special cases of the general method proposed. The applicability of the method described was demonstrated by designing error detection circuits of binary adders with different error models.

The description of the functional error model is simple if the error detection circuit has to detect all single gate faults. In this case, the maximal classes of elements of the circuit considered with one output for each class are to be determined. If the outputs of every maximal class are replaced, one after the other, by their negated outputs, the respective functions implemented by the combinational circuit are the functions of the error model. The error model then contains only just as many functions as there are different maximal classes with one output. However, this approach is not suitable for other, more specific, failure assumptions.

It is also possible to reduce the overhead for error detection circuits by weakening the requirements of the error detection. In doing so, the error model can be restricted to the most probable or most dangerous errors. Another interesting possibility is demonstrated by specifying that errors of the monitored circuit need to be detected only if certain bit patterns are applied. For other bit patterns additional don't-care conditions can then arise which can be utilized for the optimization of the error-detecting function.

An error latency period has then to be accepted, and so it may be convenient to require that the error detection circuit detects its faults for an input set that is an off-line test set. Off-line test sets for simple fault models may be automatically generated. In this way, the proposed method can be adapted to an available number of gates for error detection, as is sometimes necessary in a gate-array design.

The proposed method of error detection with weakened requirements was again applied to the design of error detection circuits for binary adders. It shows that for the weakened requirements the cost of error detection lies between 100 and 20 per cent of the total hardware costs of the monitored circuit. Also, the existing redundancy of a circuit can reasonably be utilized in the design of an error detection circuit. This was demonstrated for a carry-look-ahead adder.

THREE

SEQUENTIAL ERROR DETECTION CIRCUITS

In this chapter we shall describe how, for an arbitrary sequential circuit with a known error model, an optimal error detection circuit can be systematically determined.

Sequential circuits are modelled by abstract automata. As in the case of combinational circuits, the proposed method for the design of error detection circuits is effective in detecting every fault from an arbitrarily specified set of technical faults. To every fault in the given set of faults, an error automaton is assigned. The error automaton corresponding to a specific fault is the automaton implemented by the monitored sequential circuit in the presence of this fault. Thus the set of technical faults considered here can be functionally described by a corresponding set of error automata, the functional error model. The concept of the functional error model is explained in detail in the Appendix.

The error detection circuit detects when the monitored circuit exhibits an incorrect output for the first time, which is a possible output of one of the error automata of the functional error model. For all other incorrect outputs that are not outputs of any error automaton of the functional error model the error detection circuit remains undetermined. After the detection of the first error the behaviour of the error detection automaton is also not determined. The error detection circuit can be adequately described by a partially defined automaton which is to be optimized by usual CAD methods.

As in the case of combinational circuits, the proposed method is optimal. For a given sequential circuit and a given fault set all faults are immediately detected if they change the output to be erroneous for the first time. All possible don't-care conditions are used for optimization of the error detection circuit. Again, we suppose that the error detection circuit works correctly.

The error detection automaton of a monitored automaton with a given functional error model can be determined from a step-by-step modification of the monitored automaton and a CAD optimization of the modified automaton. In no design step does the modified automaton possess more states than the monitored automaton. Therefore the design of the error detection circuit is of the same order of complexity as the design of the monitored circuit itself. Therefore a CAD design of the error detection circuit is also possible if the monitored automaton is CAD designed. Since the proposed method is much more simple if the states of the monitored automaton are observable, we distinguish here between sequential circuits with observable and non-observable states.

3.1 BASIC NOTIONS OF AUTOMATA THEORY

Sequential circuits will be theoretically described by abstract automata. In this chapter some notions and notations of automata theory will be used extensively so they will now be introduced. More detailed introductions to automata theory are, for example, given in Gill (1962), Harrison (1965), Kohavi (1978), Zander (1982) and Gössel (1991b).

An initial deterministic automaton A is defined by $A = (X, Y, Z, z_0, f, g)$, where the input, output and state sets are X, Y and Z, respectively. The initial state is z_0, $z_0 \in Z$, the state transition function is f, $f: Z \times X \to Z$ and the output function is g, $g: Z \times X \to Y$. If no output function is defined then $A = (X, Z, z_0, f)$ is called a half-automaton or a state-automaton.

We suppose that the automaton A operates synchronously at discrete times t, $t = 0, 1, 2, \ldots$. Then the next state $z(t + 1)$ at time $t + 1$ is determined by the previous state $z(t)$ at time t and by the input $x(t)$ at time t as

$$z(t + 1) = f(z(t), x(t))$$

For the output $y(t)$ at time t one has

$$y(t) = g(z(t), x(t))$$

The present output $y(t)$ is a function of the present state $z(t)$ and the present input $x(t)$. For $t = 0$ the automaton A is in its initial state $z(0) = z_0$.

For a sequence $p = x_1 x_2 \cdots x_n$ of inputs, which is called in automata theory an input word $p \in X^*$, from the set of all finite inputs words X^* over the alphabet X the state transition function f and the output function g are 'extended'. In this book we use the following different extensions:

$$f^*(z, p) = f^*(z, x_1 x_2 \cdots x_n) = z_1 z_2 \cdots z_n$$

with

$$z_1 = f(z, x_1)$$
$$z_2 = f(z_1, x_2) = f(f(z, x_1), x_2)$$
$$\vdots$$
$$z_n = f(z_{n-1}, x_n) = f(f(\cdots f(f(z, x_1), x_2)\cdots)x_n)$$
$$g^*(z, p) = g^*(z, x_1 \cdots x_n) = y_1 \cdots y_n$$

with

$$y_1 = g(z, x_1)$$
$$y_2 = g(z_1, x_2) = g(f(z, x_1), x_2)$$
$$\vdots$$
$$y_n = g(z_{n-1}, x_n) = g(f(\cdots f(f(z, x_1), x_2)\cdots)x_n)$$

$$f(z, p) = f(z, x_1 \cdots x_n) = f(f(\cdots f(f(z, x_1), x_2)\cdots)x_n) = z_n$$

and

$$g(z, p) = g(z, x_1 \cdots x_n) = g(f(\cdots f(f(z, x_1), x_2)\cdots)x_n) = y_n$$

$f(z, p) \in Z$ denotes the state the automaton A has reached after the input word $p = x_1 \cdots x_n$ was applied to A. $g(z, p) \in Y$ denotes the last output symbol if the input sequence submitted to A was $p = x_1 \cdots x_n$, $p \in X^*$. On the other hand, $f^*(z, p) \in Z^*$ and $g^*(z, p) \in Y^*$ describe a sequence or a word of states and a sequence of outputs or an output word, respectively. The set of reachable states Z_r of an automaton $A = (X, Y, Z, z_0, f, g)$ is formally determined by

$$Z_r = \{z/z = f(z_0, p) \text{ with } p \in X^*\}$$

The important concept of equivalence between states and automata allow us to reduce or to minimize automata. This concept is discussed below.

States with the same input/output behaviour are called equivalent. Let $A = (X, Y, Z, f, g)$ and $B = (X, Y, Z', f', g')$ be automata; then the states $z \in Z$ (of the automaton A) and $z' \in Z'$ (of the automaton B) are equivalent if, for all $p \in X^*$,

$$g(z, p) = g'(z', p)$$

The automata A and B are called equivalent if for every state $z \in Z$ of the automaton A there exists a state $z' \in Z'$ of the automaton B and if for every state $z' \in Z'$ of the automaton B there exists a state $z \in Z$ of the automaton A, such that z and z' are equivalent. For $A = B$, any two states $z, z' \in Z$ of an automaton are equivalent if, for all $p \in X^*$,

$$g(z, p) = g(z', p)$$

is satisfied.

The equivalence of states defines an equivalence relation on the set of states of an automaton. Equivalent states are combined within an equivalence class. Automata that do not have any pair of equivalent states are called reduced or state-minimized automata. These are automata where the classes of equivalent states each consist of exactly one state. For a given input/output behaviour, a reduced automaton has the smallest possible number of states. Starting from a non-reduced automaton, one obtains an equivalent reduced automaton by replacing the states of the automaton to be reduced by states representing their equivalence classes.

In technical applications as well as within the contents of this book, the automata to be implemented are very frequently only partially defined. For certain inputs and states for a given problem, it is not completely specified how the automaton will respond, because such a corresponding input–state combination does not occur in the specification considered. Also, the behaviour of the automaton may no longer be of interest after a certain state has been reached. Realistically, one assumes, however, that the combinations for which the behaviour is not specified are known.

If $A = (X, Y, Z, f, g)$ is an automaton and if for $z \in Z, x \in X$ the successor state of z is not defined, then one writes

$$f(z, x) = \text{—(don't-care condition)}$$

and for an undefined output

$$g(z, x) = \text{—(don't-care condition)}$$

In an implemented circuit, however, the behaviour of the circuit is of course specified for every conceivable input–state combination, provided the design rules known to the engineer have been adhered to in the design. If a partially defined automaton A is implemented by a sequential circuit A_s, then the behaviour of the sequential circuit A_s must correspond with that of the partially defined automaton for those input–state combinations for which A is defined. For the input–state combinations for which A is not defined, i.e. where don't-care conditions are given, the behaviour of A may in principle be arbitrarily specified by replacing the don't-care conditions with arbitrary values of the permissible alphabets of Z and Y.

It should be possible to implement circuits at as low a cost as possible. Therefore one attempts to fix don't-care conditions in such a way that the circuit to be implemented becomes both simple and cheap, and especially to attempt to minimize the number of states. Thus, it is an important and already well-investigated problem in the theory of partially defined automata to find, for a partially defined automaton, its simplest implementation as a sequential circuit, with the smallest possible number of states.

For equivalent states and equivalence classes of the states of completely defined automata, there are corresponding compatible states and maximal compatibility classes of the states of partially defined automata. If in the reduction of a completely defined automaton its states are replaced by equivalence classes of states, then in the reduction of a partially defined automaton its states are likewise replaced by maximal compatibility classes.

Let $A = (X, Y, Z, f, g)$ and $B = (X, Y, Z', f', g')$ be partially defined automata; then the states $z \in Z$ (of A) and $z' \in Z'$ (of B) are compatible if, for all $p \in X^*$ whose input is defined for both the state z and the state z',

$$g(z, p) = g'(z', p) \qquad \text{if both } g(z, p) \text{ and } g'(z', p) \text{ are defined}$$

For $A = B$, any two states of an automaton A are called compatible if, for all $p \in X^*$ whose input is defined in both the state z and the state z',

$$g(z, p) = g(z', p) \qquad \text{if both } g(z, p) \text{ and } g(z', p) \text{ are defined}$$

The compatibility of states is not transitive; this means that 'z_1 is compatible with z_2' and 'z_2 is compatible with z_3' does not imply 'z_1 is compatible with z_3'. Therefore the determination of maximal compatibility classes is more demanding than that of equivalence classes of states of a completely defined automaton. The basically simple method requires high computational cost for greater numbers of states. To reduce this for great numbers of states, approximational methods are used.

Methods for the state reduction of partially defined automata are usually carried out by a computer and can be utilized by a user without detailed knowledge of the method itself.

3.2 SEQUENTIAL CIRCUITS WITH OBSERVABLE STATES

3.2.1 General Case

The determination of an error detection circuit for a given sequential circuit with observable states will now be described according to Gössel (1991a). Since the states of the considered automaton are observable, the state behaviour and the output function of a given automaton could be separately monitored by an error-detecting automaton D and an error-detecting combinational function ψ, respectively, as shown in Fig. 3.1.

Let $X \subseteq X$ be the set of interesting inputs, let $Z_r = \{z/z = f(z_0, p),\ p \in X^*\}$ be the set of states reachable from z_0 and let $F(A) = \{A_0, A_1, \ldots, A_n\}$ be the error model of A. Then $A_1, \ldots, A_n$ are those automata that may be implemented by the circuit A_s instead of A if a technical fault occurs. $A_0 = A$ is called the standard automaton. (The notion of a functional error model of a circuit and different error models corresponding to different technical fault assumptions are discussed in the Appendix.)

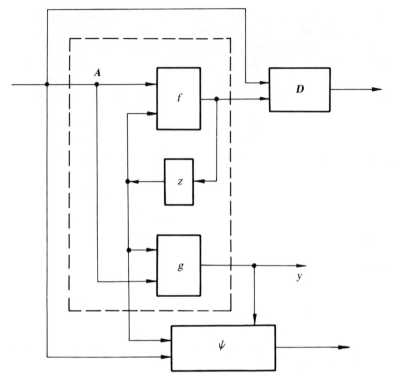

Figure 3.1 Error detection circuit for a sequential circuit with observable states.

The error-detecting automaton $D = (X \times Z, \{0, 1\}, Z, f_D, g_D)$ for monitoring the state behaviour of A is defined by

$$f_D(z, (x, z')) = \begin{cases} z' & \text{for } z \in Z_r, x \in X \text{ and } z' = f(z, x) \\ -(\text{don't care}) & \text{otherwise} \end{cases} \quad (3.1)$$

$$g_D(z, (x, z')) =$$

$$\begin{cases} 0 & \text{for } z \in Z_r, \ x \in X \text{ and } z' = f(z, x) \\ 1 & \text{for } z \in Z_r, \ x \in X \text{ and } \exists A_i \in F(A) \text{ with} \\ & (z' = f_i(z, x) \neq f(z, x) \text{ or } z = z_0 \\ & \text{and } z' = f_i(z_{0i}, x) \neq f(z_0, x) \\ -(\text{don't care}) & \text{otherwise} \end{cases} \quad (3.2)$$

The automaton D is partially defined and possesses exactly the same number of states as the monitored automaton A. It is interesting to note that the state mapping function f_D and the output function g_D of D depend on $z(t-1)$, $x(t-1)$ and $z' = z(t)$.

The error-detecting function $\psi\colon X \times Z \times Y \to \{0, 1\}$ is defined by

$\psi(x, z, y) =$

$$\begin{cases} 0 & \text{for } z \in Z_r, x \in X \text{ and } y = g(z, x) \\ 1 & \text{for } z \in Z_r, x \in X \text{ and } \exists A_i \in F(A) \text{ with } y = g_i(z, x)) \neq g(z, x) \\ \text{— (don't care)} & \text{otherwise.} \end{cases}$$

$$(3.3)$$

In this way we have $x = x(t)$, $y = y(t)$, $z = z(t)$.

Since error-detecting circuits for combinational circuits were investigated in detail in Chapter 2, in the rest of this chapter we are only concerned with the design of the error-detecting automaton D for monitoring the state behaviour of a given automaton A.

To illustrate the proposed method, consider the following example. Let A_s be a sequential circuit for implementing the half-automaton $A = (X = \{0, 1\}$, $Z = \{00, 01, 10, 11\}$, $z_0 = 00$, $f)$ with

$$f = (f_1, f_2)$$

$$z_1(t + 1) = f_1(z_1(t), z_2(t), x(t)) = (\bar{x}(t) \vee z_1(t)) \wedge z_2(t)$$

$$z_2(t + 1) = f_1(z_2(t), z_2(t), x(t)) = (x(t) \wedge \bar{z}_1(t)) \vee (\bar{x}(t) \wedge z_2(t))$$

Figure 3.2 shows the basic design of the circuit A_s where the combinational circuit f_s implements the function f described in Table 3.1. Figure 3.3 shows the automata graph of the automaton A.

We suppose that only single-bit errors during a state transition of A can occur. Then the error model $F(A)$ is given by $F(A) = \{A_0 = A, A_1, \ldots, A_{16}\}$ where the state graphs of the automata $A_1, \ldots, A_{16}$ are shown in Fig. 3.4. The automata $A_i = (X, Z, z_0, f_i)$, $i = 1, \ldots, 16$, differ from the automaton A in that differences in the state transition occur in exactly one bit each. The initial state of all automata A_i of the error model is assumed to be 00.

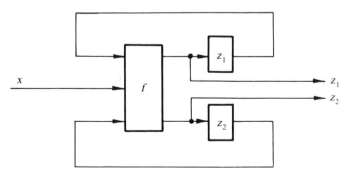

Figure 3.2 Example of a sequential circuit.

Table 3.1

	z_1	0	0	1	1
x	z_2	0	1	0	1
0		0	1	0	1
		0	1	0	1
1		0	0	0	1
		1	1	0	0

The automaton A_1, for instance, differs from the automaton A in that A_1 changes from the state 00 to the state 01 upon input 0 whereas A would otherwise remain in state 00. States 00 and 01 differ by exactly one bit.

We now determine the partially determined automaton D by a step-by-step modification of the state diagram of the automaton A of Fig. 3.3. According to the first lines of Eqs (3.1) and (3.2), we substitute an arrow marked by (x, z'), 0 for an arrow leading from z to $z' = f(z, x)$ which is marked by an x in Fig. 3.5. This modification of A guarantees that the automaton D does not indicate an error as long as the sequential circuit A_s correctly implements the automaton A.

We then take into account the errors of the error model $F(A)$. For every automaton $A_i \in F(A)$, $i = 1, \ldots, 16$, we modify the state diagram of Fig. 3.5 in such states z for which we have $z' = f_i(z, x) \neq f(z, x)$.

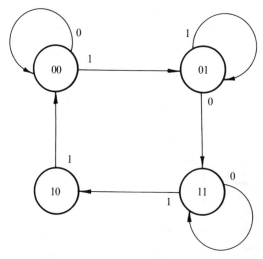

Figure 3.3 Automaton graph of the correct automaton A.

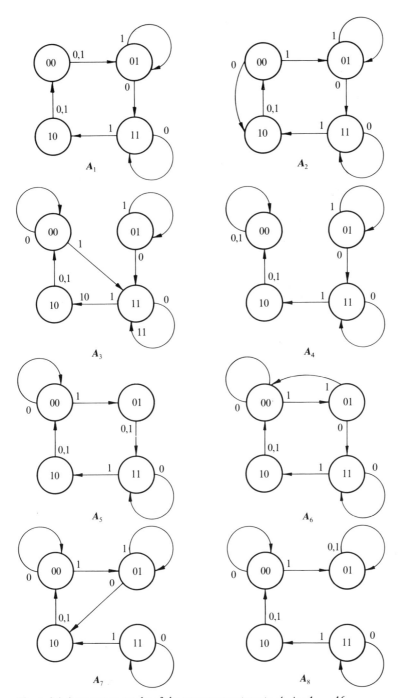

Figure 3.4 Automaton graphs of the erroneous automata A_i, $i = 1, \ldots, 16$.

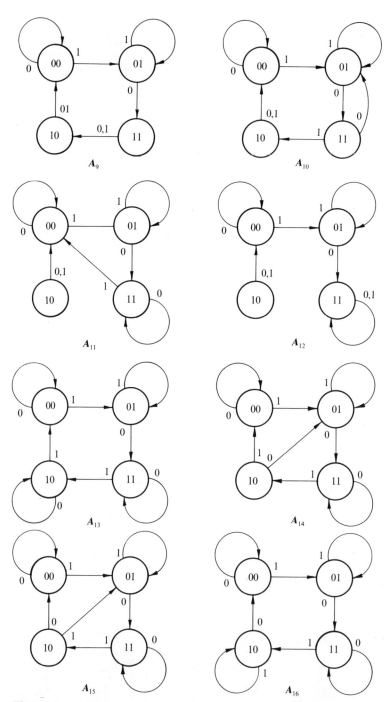

Figure 3.4 *continued*

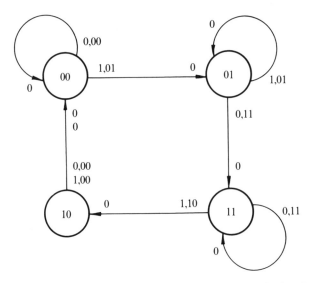

Figure 3.5 First step of the modification of A into D, reflecting the correct behaviour.

According to the second lines of Eqs (3.1) and (3.2) we add an arrow marked with (x, z'), 1 arising from state z, the end point of which remains undefined. Thus for the automaton A_1 we have $01 = f_1(00, 0) \neq f(00, 0) = 00$ for $z = (00)$. Therefore an arrow marked with $(0, 01)$, 1 and with a free end is added at state 00. This modification is shown in Fig. 3.6.

The partially defined automaton of Fig. 3.6 outputs 0, 0, 0, ... as long as the sequential circuit A_s realizes $A_0 = A$. In the case of a technical fault which results in an erroneous implementation of A_1 instead of A, this fault is detected by an output of 1 if in state 00 an input signal 0 is submitted to A_s. This state transition $f_1(00, 0) = 01$ of A_1 is the only one that differs from corresponding state transitions of A.

Now all of the remaining automata $A_2, \ldots, A_{16}$ of the error model $F(A)$ can be taken into account in a similar way. The resulting diagram of the error detecting automaton D is shown in Fig. 3.7. The automaton D is partially determined.

If we simultaneously have

$$f_D(z, (x, z')) = \text{---(don't care)}$$

and

$$g_D(z, (x, z')) = \text{---(don't care)}$$

the corresponding arrows in Fig. 3.7 are omitted and all state transitions not drawn in the diagram of Fig. 3.7 are undetermined with respect to their

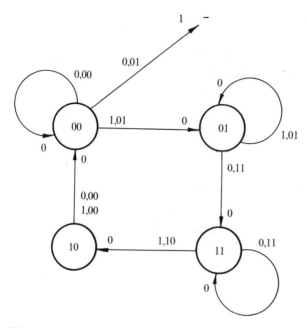

Figure 3.6 Second step of the modification of *A* into *D* due to the automaton A_1 of the error model.

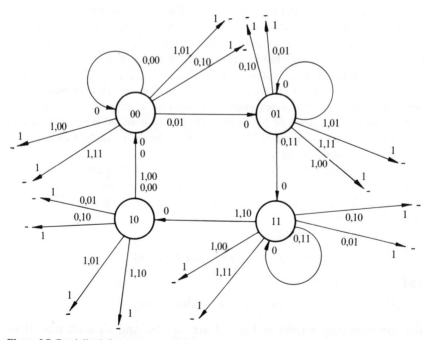

Figure 3.7 Partially defined error detection automaton.

outputs and to their end points. Thus, for example, we have

$$f_D(00, (0, 11)) = \text{—(don't care)}$$

$$g_D(00, (0, 11)) = \text{—(don't care)}$$

since there is no automaton A_k of the error model $F(A)$ with a production rule of the form

$$11 = f_k(00, 0)$$

Table 3.2

z	x	z'	$f_D(z, x, z')$	$g_D(z, x, z')$	$A_i \in f(A)$
00	0	00	00	0	A
00	0	01	—	1	A_1
00	0	10	—	1	A_2
00	0	11	—	—	—
00	1	00	—	1	A_4
00	1	01	01	0	A
00	1	10	—	—	—
00	1	11	—	1	A_3
01	0	00	—	—	—
01	0	01	—	1	A_8
01	0	10	—	1	A_7
01	0	11	11	0	A
01	1	00	—	1	A_6
01	1	01	01	0	A
01	1	10	—	—	—
01	1	11	—	1	A_5
10	0	00	00	0	A
10	0	01	—	1	A_{14}
10	0	10	—	1	A_{13}
10	0	11	—	—	—
10	1	00	00	0	A
10	1	01	—	1	A_{15}
10	1	10	—	1	A_{16}
10	1	11	—	—	—
11	0	00	—	—	—
11	0	01	—	1	A_{10}
11	0	10	—	1	A_9
11	0	11	11	0	A
11	1	00	—	1	A_{11}
11	1	01	—	—	—
11	1	10	10	0	A
11	1	11	—	1	A_{12}

Table 3.3

z	x	z'	fD_{min}	gD_{min}
A	0	00	A	0
A	0	01	—	1
A	0	10	—	1
A	0	11	A	0
A	1	00	—	1
A	1	01	A	0
A	1	10	B	0
A	1	11	—	1
B	0	00	A	0
B	0	01	—	1
B	0	10	—	1
B	0	11	—	—
B	1	00	A	0
B	1	01	—	1
B	1	10	—	1
B	1	11	—	—

which would obviously involve a 2-bit error of A. The corresponding arrow starting at state 00 marked with $(0, 11)$, — and with an undetermined end point is omitted in Fig. 3.7.

Like the standard automaton A, the automaton $D = (X \times Y, \{0, 1\}, Z = \{00, 01, 10, 11\}, f_D, g_D)$ has only four states. Table 3.2 shows the functions f_D and g_D. The error-detecting automaton, D_{min}, whose implementation is the desired error detection circuit, is obtained from D by state reduction.

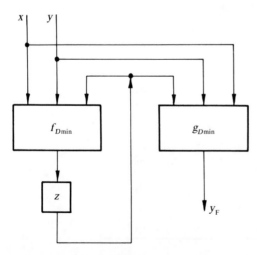

Figure 3.8 Optimized error detection automaton.

Table 3.4

z	x	z'	$fD_{min}(z, x, y)$	$gD_{min}(z, x, y)$
0	0	00	0	0
0	0	01	—	1
0	0	10	—	1
0	0	11	0	0
0	1	00	—	1
0	1	01	0	0
0	1	10	1	0
0	1	11	—	1
1	0	00	0	0
1	0	01	—	1
1	0	10	—	1
1	0	11	—	—
1	1	00	0	0
1	1	01	—	1
1	1	10	—	1
1	1	11	—	—

Since the states 00, 01 and 11 of D are compatible they are combined into a compatibility class $A = \{00, 01, 11\}$. The state 10 is not compatible with any other state, forming a separate compatibility class $B = \{10\}$. For $D_{min} = (X \times Z, \{0, 1\}, \{A, B\}, A, fD_{min}, gD_{min})$ the representation of fD_{min} and gD_{min} given in Table 3.3 is then obtained from Table 3.2. The error detecting automation D_{min} has only two states whereas the automaton A to be monitored has four states.

If we encode $A = 0$, $B = 1$ then for D_{min} we obtain the implementation shown in Fig. 3.8 with the functions fD_{min} and gD_{min} now of Boolean type, as listed in Table 3.4.

3.2.2 Heuristic Methods

Now we discuss different heuristic methods for the design of an error-detecting automaton $D = (X \times Z, \{0, 1\}, Z_D, Z_{0D}, f_D, g_D)$ for monitoring the state behaviour of an automaton $A = (X, Y, Z, z_0, f, g)$ with the functional error model $F(A) = \{A, A_1, \ldots, A_k\}$, $A_i = \{X, Y, Z_i, z_{0i}, f_i, g_i\}$. For simplicity of presentation we now assume $Z = Z_1 = \cdots = Z_k$.

These methods are specializations of the general case so far described and were inspired by Horwarth (1985). The methods may also be interpreted as modifications of duplication and comparison.

To begin with we define a coding function Cod,

$$\text{Cod}: Z \times X \times Z \to U$$

with

$$\text{Cod}(z, x, z') \neq \text{Cod}(z, x, z''), \; z' \neq z'' \qquad (3.4)$$

if there exists an error automaton $A_i \in F(A)$ such that

$$z' = f_i(z, x) \neq z'' = f(z, x) \qquad \text{for } z \in Z_r$$

Thereby Z_r, $Z_r \subseteq Z$ as previously defined, is the set of states of A reachable from z_0 and the set U is the range of the coding function.

For a given automaton A and a given error model $F(A)$ a coding function for which Eq. (3.4) is valid can be determined by solving the standard graph theoretical problem of colouring the graph $G = (V, E)$, where the set of nodes V is defined by

$$V = \{(z, x, z')/z \in Z_r, x \in X, z' \in Z\} \qquad (3.5)$$

The nodes (z, x, z') and (z, x, z'') of G are connected by an edge, if there exists an A_i, $A_i \in F(A)$ such that we have

$$z' = f_i(z, x) \neq z'' = f(z, x)$$

and the set E of edges of G is

$$E = \{(z, x, z'), (z, x, z'')/z' \neq z'', \quad A_i \in F(A), \quad z' = f_i(z, x) \neq z'' = f(z, x)\} \quad (3.6)$$

Let Col: $V \to U'$ be a colouring where U' is the set of colours of G such that different colours are assigned to different nodes v_1 and v_2. If v_1 and v_2 are connected by an edge, i.e. $(v_1, v_2) \in E$, this implies

$$\text{Col}(v_1) \neq \text{Col}(v_2) \qquad (3.7)$$

Put $U' = U$ and

$$\text{Cod}(z, x, z') = \text{Col}(z, x, z')$$

Figure 3.9 shows a possible functional block diagram of the error detecting automaton D for monitoring the state behaviour of A_s before minimization.

As long as the sequential circuit A_s correctly implements the state behaviour of A the comparator COMP will output 0. If A_s implements an automaton A_i of the error model $F(A)$ then the comparator COMP outputs 1 if an input x is submitted to A_s in state z for which we have $f_i(z, x) \neq f(z, x)$. It must be mentioned that the don't-care conditions in Eqs (3.1) and (3.2) are fixed before minimizing D by the choice of the function Cod = Col and by the functional block diagram of Fig. 3.9. The number of nodes of the graph G which is to be coloured is $|Z_r|^2 \cdot |X|$, but it is easy to see that the necessary number of different colours is less or equal to $|Z|$. If we put $U' = Z_r$ and $\text{Col}(z, x, z') = z'$ for $z, z' \in Z_r$ and $x \in X$ the functional block diagram of Fig. 3.9 reduces to duplication of the state machine of A and then comparison, as represented in Fig. 3.10.

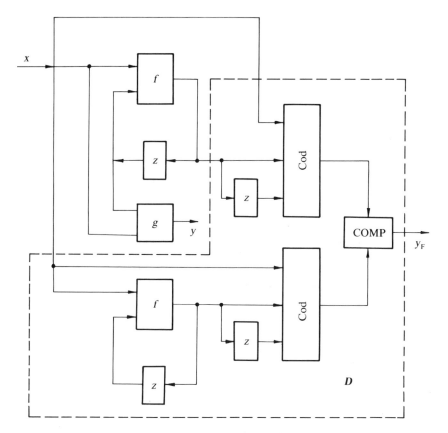

Figure 3.9 Heuristic error detection automaton before minimization.

Since duplication (of the state machine of A) and comparison is a special case of the proposed method the minimization of D results in an automaton D_{min} with at most $|Z|$ states, where $|Z|$ is the number of states of A. Again, the don't-care conditions in Eqs (3.1) and (3.2) are fixed before minimization of D. From this point of view, D_{min} is not optimal.

Suppose that the coding function, called Cod1, depends upon z only:

$$\text{Cod1}: Z \rightarrow U$$

Then we have, instead of Eq. (3.4),

$$\text{Cod1}(z') \neq \text{Cod1}(z'') \qquad (3.8)$$

if there exists an $A_i \in F(A)$, $z \in Z_r$, $x \in X$ such that

$$z' = f_i(z, x) \neq z'' = f(z, x)$$

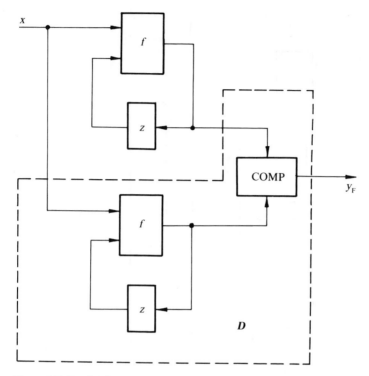

Figure 3.10 Duplication and comparison as a specialization of Fig. 3.9.

Like the general case, a coding function Cod1 may be determined as a colouring Col1 of graph $G_1 = (V_1, E_1)$, where

$$V_1 = \{z \mid z \in Z\} \tag{3.9}$$

Two nodes, z' and z'' such that $z' \neq z''$, of G_1 are connected by an edge if there exists an automaton A_i of the error model $F(A)$, a state z, $z \in Z_r$, and an input $x \in X$ such that

$$z' = f_i(z, x) \neq z'' = f(z, x), \qquad z \in Z_r$$

$$E_1 = \{(z', z'') \mid z' \neq z'', A_i \in F(A), z \in Z_r, x \in X, z' = f_i(z, x), z'' = f(z, x)\} \tag{3.10}$$

If Col1 is a colouring of the graph G_1, then all nodes connected by an edge are differently coloured, $(z', z'') \in E_1$ implies $Col1(z') \neq Col1(z'')$, and if we put

$$Cod1(z) = Col1(z) \qquad \text{for } z \in Z$$

the condition (3.4) for the coding function Cod1 is obviously satisfied.

The graph G_1 possesses $|Z_r|$, $|Z_r| \leqslant |Z|$, nodes. A colouring of this relatively small graph is much more easily computed than the graph G with

$|Z_r|^2 \cdot |X|$ nodes. Generally, less colours are needed to colour G than G_1, however.

A simple functional block diagram for monitoring the state behaviour of A is shown in Fig. 3.11. The output function of A is omitted. The difference from duplication and comparison is that instead of the states of the original and the duplicated half-automaton the corresponding codings of these states are compared.

The automaton D is to be minimized into D_{min}. D_{min} may be much simpler than A. Another functional block diagram for monitoring the state behaviour of an automaton A where the coding function Cod according to Eq. (3.8) depends on z only is shown in Fig. 3.12. The coding of the actual state $\text{Cod}(z(t-1))$ is compared with the coding $\text{Cod}(f(z(t-2), x(t-2)))$.

In general the word length of the register R_1 is smaller than the word length of the register R of the original automaton and of the corresponding error detecting automaton D in Fig. 3.11. However, in Fig. 3.12 we have assumed that the outputs of the register R of the automaton A to be monitored are accessible. The block diagram of Fig. 3.13 only monitors the combinational function f of the automaton A.

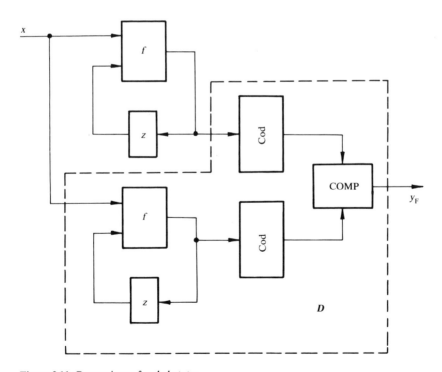

Figure 3.11 Comparison of coded states.

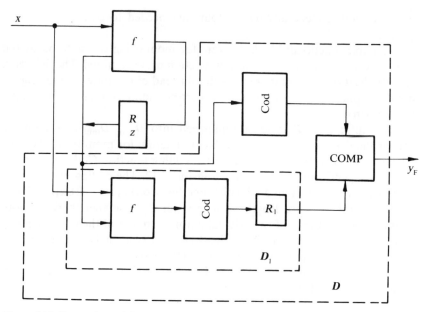

Figure 3.12 Comparison of the coded actual and predicted states.

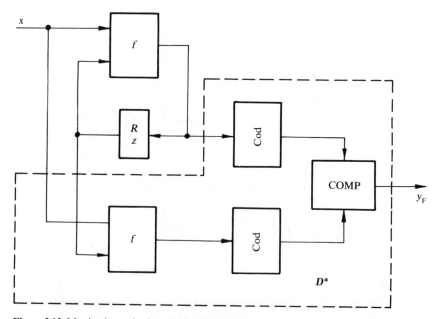

Figure 3.13 Monitoring only the combinational function f.

If both the automaton A and the combinational circuit $D*$ are correctly working, the comparator proves that

$$\text{Cod}(f(z(t-1), x(t-1))) = \text{Cod } z(t)$$

is valid. However, an incorrect output of the register R for an correct input cannot be detected.

If only the automaton D_1 in Fig. 3.12 is optimized the method described is similar to duplication and comparison. Generally, though, the optimization of the automaton D of Fig. 3.12 results in a simpler error detecting automaton. (In Parekhij *et al.* (1991) the graph $G_1 = (V_1, E_1)$ was independently introduced as the 'constraint graph' on Gössel (1991a). In Parekhij *et al.* (1991) the error detection circuit is to be determined as the state minimal monitored automaton under the assumption that states connected by an edge of the constraint graph are compatible.)

Sometimes it is more convenient to determine the 'difference'

$$\Phi(z(t-1), x(t-1)) := \text{Cod}(f(z(t-1), x(t))) - \text{Cod}(z(t-1))$$

between the coding of the state $z(t-1)$ and the predicted next state $f(z(t-1), x(t-1))$ instead of $\text{Cod}(f(z(t-1), x(t-1)))$, where the operation $-$ is a subtraction in a suitable field. Figure 3.14 shows a possible functional block diagram for monitoring the state behaviour of an automaton A by use of $\Phi(z(t-1), x(t-1))$.

As a first example, we determine the error-detecting automaton D of a Gray-code counter $A = (\{0, 1\}, \{00, 01, 10, 11\}, 00, f)$ with four states; the state diagram of this is shown in Fig. 3.15. If the input $x(t-1) = 1$ is submitted to A then the states $z(t-1)$ and $z(t)$ differ by exactly one bit. A remains in its state, if its input is zero.

We assume that only single-bit errors in state transitions occur. The error model $F(A) = \{A_0 = A, A_1, \ldots, A_{16}\}$ consists, apart from the correct automaton of 16 erroneous automata, of $A_1, \ldots, A_{16}$; $A_i = (\{0, 1\}, \{00, 01, 10, 11\}, 00, f_i)$, $i = 1, \ldots, 16$. The state diagram of A_1 is represented in Fig. 3.16.

A_1 differs from A in that we have $f_1(00, 0) = 01$ for A_1 instead of $f(00, 0) = 00$ for A. All of the other state transitions are identical. Thus we have

$$f_1(z, x) = \begin{cases} 01 & \text{for } z = 00 \text{ and } x = 0 \\ f(z, x) & \text{otherwise} \end{cases}$$

In a shortened form we describe A_1 by $f_1(00, 0) = 01$, the only value for which the state transition function f_1 of A_1 is different from the state transition function f of A.

The other automata A_i, $i = 2, \ldots, 16$, can similarly be described by the values of the function f_i for which they are different from f of A. For

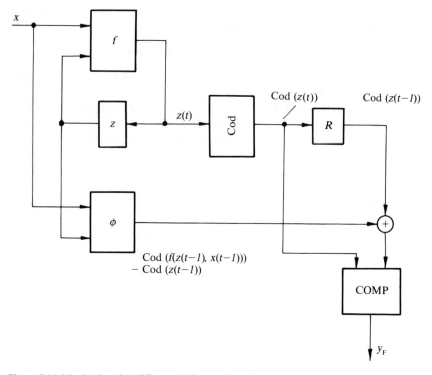

Figure 3.14 Monitoring the 'difference' of successive states.

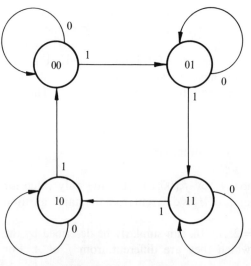

Figure 3.15 State diagram of a Gray-code counter.

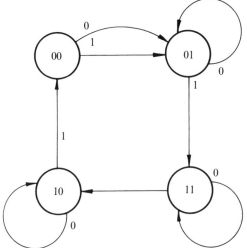

Figure 3.16 Erroneous automaton A_1.

$i = 1, \ldots, 16$ these values are

$$f_1(00, 0) = 01, \quad f_2(00, 0) = 10, \quad f_3(00, 1) = 00, \quad f_4(00, 1) = 11$$
$$f_5(01, 0) = 00, \quad f_6(01, 0) = 11, \quad f_7(01, 1) = 01, \quad f_8(01, 1) = 10$$
$$f_9(11, 0) = 01, \quad f_{10}(11, 0) = 10, \quad f_{11}(11, 1) = 11, \quad f_{12}(11, 1) = 00$$
$$f_{13}(10, 0) = 11, \quad f_{14}(10, 0) = 00, \quad f_{15}(10, 1) = 10, \quad f_{16}(10, 1) = 01$$

The corresponding graph $G = (V = \{00, 01, 10, 11\}, E = \{(00, 01), (00, 10), (10, 11), (01, 11)\})$ to be coloured is shown in Fig. 3.17. The vertices 00 and 01 are connected by an edge $(00, 01) \in E$, since we have

$$00 = f(00, 0) \neq f_1(00, 0) = 01$$

The vertices 00 and 11 are not connected by an edge, because $z \in Z$, $x \in X$, $A_i \in F(A)$ does not exist such that we have

$$00 = f(z, x) \neq f_i(z, x) = 11$$

All the other edges between the vertices of G can be similarily understood.

The graph G can be coloured using two colours called red and green as in Fig. 3.17. The parity $P(z) = z_1 \oplus z_2$ of the 'red states' is 0 while the parity of the 'green state' is 1. The functional block diagram of the error detecting circuit D for monitoring the state behaviour of the Gray-code counter is shown in Fig. 3.18.

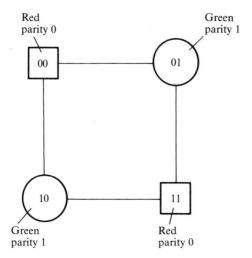

Red
parity 0

Green
parity 1

00 — 01

10 — 11

Green
parity 1

Red
parity 0

Figure 3.17 Coloured graph of the Gray-code counter.

The block diagram of Fig. 3.18 is equivalent to the block diagram of Fig. 3.19. The simplification of Fig. 3.19 is based on the fact that the parity $P(z(t))$ of the state $z(t)$ at time t can be determined by

$$P(z(t)) = P(z(t-1)) \oplus x(t-1)$$

This can easily be seen from the state diagram of A in Fig. 3.15.

As the next example we consider here the design of an error-detecting circuit for a modulo-2^n counter C_n. We suppose that the combinational part of the modulo-2^n counter is implemented as a ripple adder cascading n 1-bit adders $A_0, \ldots, A_{n-1}$ as shown, for $n = 3$, in Fig. 3.20. Furthermore, we suppose that the carry-out output c_i and the sum outputs of the 1-bit adders are separately implemented without any common gates. We assume that at most one gate of the adders $A_0, \ldots, A_{n-1}$ or of the registers $R_0, \ldots, R_{n-1}$ is faulty at any time. Then at most one of the sum outputs or c_i of one of the adders or of one of the registers may be erroneous.

Let $z(t)$ be the correct next state of the correct state $z(t-1)$ and let $z'(t)$ be an erroneous next state of $z(t-1)$. Under the assumption that only a single error of the described type occurs we have

$$(z'(t) - z(t)) \bmod 2^n \in \{\pm 1, \pm 2, \pm 4, \ldots, \pm 2^{n-1}\} \bmod 2^n$$

with

$$(-2^{n-1}) \bmod 2^n = 2^{n-1}$$

To determine a coding function Cod: $Z \to U$ for the construction of an error-detecting automaton D according to Fig. 3.11, we have to colour the

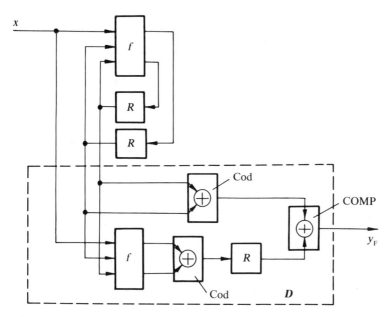

Figure 3.18 Error detection circuit for the Gray-code counter.

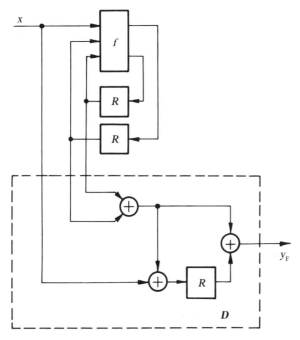

Figure 3.19 Simplified error detection circuit for the Gray-code counter.

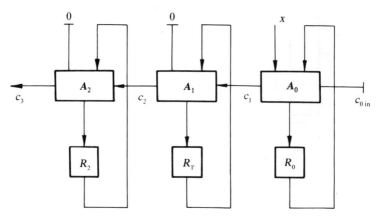

Figure 3.20 Modulo-2^3 counter C_3.

graph $G = (V, E)$ with $V = Z = \{0, 1, \ldots, 2^n - 1\}$. Two nodes v_1, v_2 of this graph G are connected by an edge, $(v_1, v_2) \in E$, if we have

$$(v_1 - v_2) \bmod 2^n \in \{\pm 1, \pm 2, \ldots, \pm 2^{n-1}\} \bmod 2^n$$

Since $(-2^{n-1}) \bmod 2^n = 2^{n-1}$, every node $v \in V$ is connected with the $2n - 1$ nodes $(v \pm 1) \bmod 2^n$, $(v \pm 2) \bmod 2^n, \ldots, (v \pm 2^{n-1}) \bmod 2^n$, respectively. Therefore at least $2n$ colours are needed to colour the corresponding graph G_n with 2^n nodes.

The graphs G_2 and G_3 are shown in Fig. 3.21. For $n = 2$ we need $2n = 4$ colours to colour the graph G_2. Therefore the word length of register R_1 in Fig. 3.11 has to be 2, which is equal to the length 2 of the register R; the constructed error detection automaton is very similar to duplication and comparison. For $n = 3$ we need at least $2n = 6$ colours to colour the graph G_3 of Fig. 3.21. However, it is relatively simple to show that we actually need eight colours. (For $n = 4$ it is left to the reader to show that 16 colours are needed to colour G_4.)

The word lengths of registers R_1 and R in Fig. 3.11 have to be equal. It can be seen again that the error-detecting automaton is very similar to duplication and comparison. We now determine the error-detecting circuit of a modulo-2 counter $C_2 = (\{0, 1\}, \{(01), (10)\}, (01), f)$ whose states are coded as elements of an 1-out-of-2 code. The state diagram of C_2 is given in Fig. 3.22.

The implementation of C_2 requires at least two binary registers with four states. The state transition of the states 00 and 11 is determined only by the concrete implementation of C_2. A possible implementation of C_2 is shown in Fig. 3.23. The state diagram of this implementation of C_2 is given

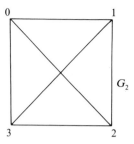

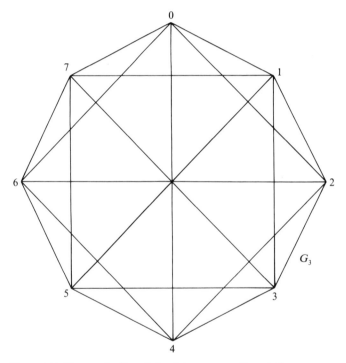

Figure 3.21 The graphs G_2 and G_3 of the counters C_2 and C_3.

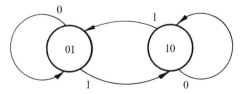

Figure 3.22 Modulo-2 counter with states from a 1-out-of-2 code.

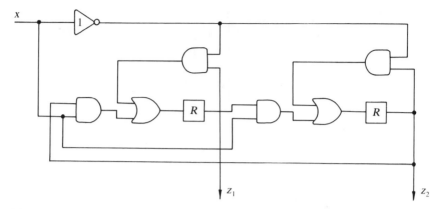

Figure 3.23 Implementation of a modulo-2 counter.

in Fig. 3.24. The set of states Z_r, reachable from $z_0 = (01)$, of the automaton C_2 is $Z_r = \{01, 10\}$.

To determine the error detection automaton D we need to modify the state diagram of C_2 into the state diagram of D only for the states that are ultimately reachable. For the states 01 and 10, reachable from z_0, all simple errors of the logical gates or of the registers of C_2 result in single-bit errors.

On the other hand, if the output of the negator marked by 1 in Fig. 3.23 is stuck-at-0 for $x = 0$, the state 11 changes into 00. However, this 2-bit error does not have to be taken into account, since the state 11 is not reachable from $z_0 = (01)$. Thus the state diagram of C_2 of Fig. 3.24 has to be modified only into the state diagram of the error detection automaton D of Fig. 3.25.

The minimization of the partially defined error detection automaton D of Fig. 3.25 results in a combinational circuit D_{min} which is independent of

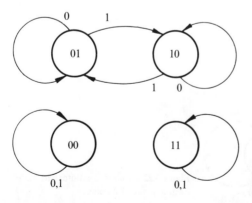

Figure 3.24 State diagram of the implementation of Fig. 3.23.

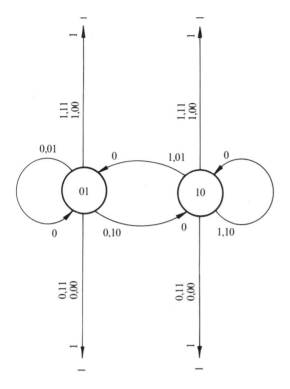

Figure 3.25 Partially defined error detection automaton before optimization.

the input x. Thus $D_{\min}$ is a code checker for a 1-out-of-2 code with

$$D_{\min} = (\{0, 1\} \times \{00, 01, 10, 11\}, \{0, 1\}, \{\phi\}, f_{\min}, g_{\min})$$

$$f_{\min}(\phi, (x, z)) = \phi \text{ for } (x, z) \in \{0, 1\} \times \{00, 01, 10, 11\}$$

$$g_{\min}(\phi, (x, z)) = \begin{cases} 0 & \text{for } z \in \{01, 10\} \\ 1 & \text{for } z \in \{00, 11\} \end{cases}$$

Of course a somewhat experienced designer of error-detecting circuits would choose a 1-out-of-2 code checker to monitor the state behaviour of this considered modulo-2 counter without any further considerations.

These simple examples were only needed to demonstrate how to apply the proposed method.

3.3 SEQUENTIAL CIRCUITS WITH NON-OBSERVABLE STATES

This section deals with the design of an optimal error-detecting circuit for a given sequential circuit, with non-observable states.

Let A_s again be a sequential circuit for implementing the automaton $A = (X, Y, Z, z_0, f, g)$. Let $F(A) = \{A_0 = A, A_1, \ldots, A_n\}$, with $A_i = (X, Y_i, Z_i, z_i, z_{0i}, f_i, g_i)$, $i = 1, \ldots, n$, be the error model of A. As in the preceding section, $A_1, \ldots, A_n$ are those automata that may be implemented by the circuit A_s instead of A if the technical failures considered should occur.

The automaton $B = \{X \times Y, \{0, 1\}, Z, z_0, f_B, g_B\}$ with the input alphabet $X \times Y$ and the output alphabet $\{0, 1\}$ is called an error-detecting automaton of A with the error model $F(A)$ if, for all $x_1, x_2, \ldots, x_m \in X \subseteq X$,

$$g_B(z_{0B}, x_1 y_1 \cdots x_m y_m) =$$

$$
\begin{cases}
0 & \text{for } y_1 = g(z_0, x_1) \text{ and } y_2 = g(z_0, x_1 x_2) \text{ and } \cdots \text{ and} \\
& y_m = g(z_0, x_1 \cdots x_m) \\
1 & \text{for } y_1 = g(z_0, x_1) \text{ and } y_2 = g(z_0, x_1 x_2) \text{ and } \cdots \text{ and} \\
& y_{m-1} = g(z_0, x_1 \cdots x_{m-1}) \text{ and } \exists A_i \in F(A) \text{ with} \\
& y_m = g_i(z_{0i}, x_1 \cdots x_m) \neq g(z_0, x_1 \cdots x_m) \\
\text{—(don't care)} & \text{otherwise} \hspace{4cm} (3.11)
\end{cases}
$$

A circuit B_s that implements B is called an error detection circuit of A. As long as the outputs of A_s are equal to the correct outputs no error is indicated according to Eq. (3.11) by the error detection automaton B. If the output of A_s for the first time is erroneous, but only if this erroneous output is an output of an error automaton of the functional error model, then the error detection automaton outputs 1, indicating the detection of an error of the considered error model. In all other cases the behaviour of the error detection automaton remains undetermined. Thus the don't care conditions in Eq. (3.11) only make sure that errors of the error model $F(A)$ are detected by the circuit B_s. After an error has been detected by the error detection circuit B_s, the latter may behave arbitrarily. (Output of 1 in the mth cycle is required only if an error according to the error model occurs in the mth cycle and if B_s has not indicated any error up to the mth cycle.)

Since the don't-care conditions in Eq. (3.11) are used for circuit optimization and since the success of an optimization generally improves with increasing number of don't-care conditions available, it is desirable to have as many of these conditions as possible. This is the reason why one allows an arbitrary behaviour of the error detection circuit after indication of the first error. The input symbols $x_1, \ldots, x_m$ are elements of a subset X of X, e.g. elements of a code.

In principle, one might permit these subsets to be time dependent or dependent on the state of A, etc. We confine ourselves to one subset in order to make the representation as clear as possible. If necessary, this dependence of the input set on time or on state can be taken into consideration in a fairly simple way.

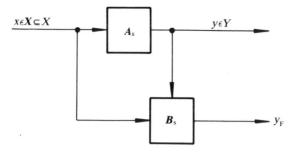

Figure 3.26 General error detection circuit.

If there is no error model available and if it is only known that the circuit A_s may be faulty in some way or other, then instead of Eq. (3.11) one has, for $x_1, \ldots, x_m \in X \subseteq X$,

$$g_B(z_{0B}, x_1 y_1 \cdots x_m y_m) =$$

$$\begin{cases} 0 & \text{for } y_1 = g(z_0, x_1) \text{ and } y_2 = g(z_0, x_1 x_2) \text{ and } \cdots \text{ and} \\ & y_m = g(z_0, x_1 \cdots x_m) \\ 1 & \text{for } y_1 = g(z_0, x_1) \text{ and } \cdots \text{ and} \\ & y_{m-1} = g(z_0, x_1 \cdots x_{m-1}) \text{ and } y_m \neq g(z_0, x_1 \cdots x_m) \quad (3.12) \\ - \text{(don't care)} & \text{otherwise} \end{cases}$$

Also, in this case, an error detection circuit that has detected an error at any time is allowed to behave arbitrarily thereafter. The basic design of an error detection circuit A_s for the automaton A is shown in Fig. 3.26.

The input and the output of A_s are connected to the error detection circuit B_s, which outputs zero if A_s operates correctly; otherwise it outputs the value 1 in the case of an incorrect operation, as defined by the error model.

In contrast to the definition of an error detection circuit given above, in Meyer and Sunderstrom (1975) it is only required that every error encountered is indicated after a delay of at most n cycles, with $n > 0$ being fixed.

3.4 ACTUAL METHOD

Let us now deal with the problem of actually determining an optimum error-detecting automaton for an arbitrary finite automaton A with the error model $F(A) = \{A_0, A_1, \ldots, A_n\}, n > 0$.

A direct translation of the error-detecting automaton B defined by Eq. (3.11) into a block diagram is shown in Fig. 3.27. It is built up of the automata $A = A_0$, $A_1, \ldots, A_n$ of the error model $F(A)$, $n + 1$ comparators, a

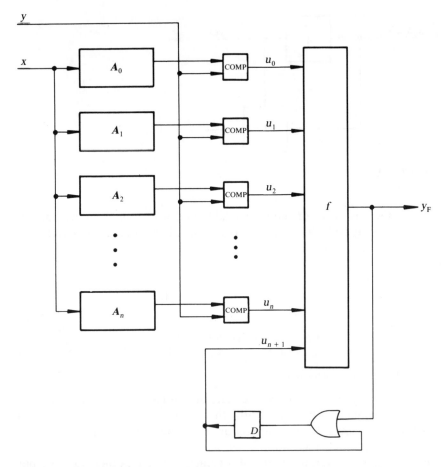

Figure 3.27 Direct implementation of Eq. (3.11).

combinational circuit with $n + 2$ binary inputs and one binary output, which implements the partially defined Boolean function f, a delay flip-flop and an (inclusive) OR element.

The input of the error detection automaton A which carries the input signal x is connected to all the automata $A_0, A_1, \ldots, A_n$ of the error model in parallel. The outputs of the automata $A_0, A_1, \ldots, A_n$ are fed to the comparators and compared with the output signal y of the circuit A_s to be monitored. A comparator outputs zero if its two input signals coincide and one if they do not. The binary output signals of the comparators are denoted by $u_0, u_1, \ldots, u_n$.

The binary output of the combinational circuit f is connected via an

OR element and a delay flip-flop to the $(n + 2)$th input of the combinational circuit f. The initial state of the delay flip-flop is zero.

At the time when the combinational circuit f outputs the first 1, the delay flip-flop changes to the 1 state, from which it cannot return because of feedback via the OR element. Therefore, after the output of the first 1 by f there will always be a 1 applied to the $(n + 2)$th input of f. For f one has

$$f(u_0, u_1, \ldots, u_{n+1}) = \begin{cases} 0 & \text{for } u_0 = 0 \text{ and } u_{n+1} = 0 \\ 1 & \text{for } u_0 = 1 \text{ and } u_1 = 0 \text{ and } u_{n+1} = 0 \\ 1 & \text{for } u_0 = 1 \text{ and } u_2 = 0 \text{ and } u_{n+1} = 0 \\ \vdots & \\ 1 & \text{for } u_0 = 1 \text{ and } u_n = 0 \text{ and } u_{n+1} = 0 \\ - \text{(don't care)} & \text{otherwise} \end{cases} \qquad (3.13)$$

In particular, the behaviour of the automaton B remains undetermined after the first output of 1.

It is obvious that the automaton B outputs the first 1 exactly when the circuit to be monitored outputs a value that is erroneous and coincides with a value output by an automaton of the error model. After the output of the first 1, the behaviour of the automaton B, as has already been pointed out, will be undetermined. The don't-care conditions can be used to optimize the automaton B. The partially defined automaton shown in Fig. 3.27 has $m_0 \cdot m_1 \cdot \cdots \cdot m_n \cdot 2$ states, where m_i is the number of states of the automaton A_i, $i = 0, \ldots, n$.

For as little as $n = 9$, $m_0 = m_1 = \cdots = m_9 = 10$, one obtains 2×10^{10} states, so in this case it is already not possible to use the well-known automated computer aided optimization methods for sequential circuits. On the other hand, it is obvious that the state-reduced partial automaton B_{red} has at most m_0 states. This is so because, if we determine the don't-care conditions of the function f in Eq. (3.13) as

$$f(u_0, u_1, \ldots, u_{n+1}) = \begin{cases} 0 & \text{for } u_0 = 0 \text{ and } u_{n+1} = 1 \\ 1 & \text{for } u_0 = 1 \text{ and } u_1 = u_2 = \cdots = u_n = 1 \end{cases} \qquad (3.14)$$

then

$$f(u_0, u_1, \ldots, u_{n+1}) = \begin{cases} 0 & \text{for } u_0 = 0 \\ 1 & \text{for } u_0 = 1 \end{cases} \qquad (3.15)$$

With this special determination of the don't-care conditions the circuit of Fig. 3.27 is equivalent to duplication and comparison. However, duplication and comparison require at most m_0 states, because in this case the error detection circuit can be built up of the reduced automaton A_{red} and one comparator.

In what follows a description is given of how, starting from definition (3.11) or from the block diagram shown in Fig. 3.27, a reduced error detection automaton A_{red} can actually be determined. To begin with, for that purpose we modify the standard automaton $A_0 = A = (X, Y, Z, z_0, f, g)$ into a partially defined automaton $C = (X \times Y, \{0, 1\}, z_0, f_c, g_c)$, which is equivalent to B but exhibits only the same number of states as the automaton A. Then the partially defined automaton C has to be minimized by the usual methods of state reduction for partially defined automata. The modification of the automaton A into the automaton B can then be carried out step by step.

Step 1 For $x \in X$, $y \in Y$, z, $z' \in Z$ we set

$$f(z, (x, y)) = z' \qquad \text{for } z' = f(z, x) \text{ and } g(z, x) = y$$

$$g_c(z, (x, y)) = 0 \qquad \text{for } g(z, x) = y$$

Graphically, this means that in the automata graph of A we replace an arrow extending from z to z', being marked by x and y, by an arrow marked by (x, y) and 0. Thus the automaton C does not indicate any errors as long as the circuit to be monitored behaves like the standard automaton $A_0 = A$.

Step 2 For each automaton $A_i \in F(A)$ we determine an error detection tree G_i which describes the difference in behaviour between A and A_i up to the first externally detectable error. The nodes of the error detection tree are the state pairs (z, z'), $z \in Z$, $z' \in Z_i$, such that z is a state of the automaton A and z' is a state of the automaton A_i. The root of the tree G_i is the pair (z_0, z_{0i}) of initial states of A and A_i. For $x \in X$, a node (z, z') of the error detection tree G_i is connected with the node $(f(z, x), f_i(z', x))$ by an arrow pointing from (z, z') to $(f(z, x), f_i(z', x))$, which is marked by x, $(g(z, x), g_i(z', x))$. If $g(z, x) \neq g_i(z', x)$, then $(f(z, x), f_i(z', x))$ is a terminal vertex of type 1. There are no arrows starting from a terminal vertex of type 1.

If $(f(z, x), f_i(z', x))$ is not a terminal vertex of type 1 and if it has already occurred in G_i (but not as a terminal vertex of type 1), then $(f(z, x), f_i(z', x))$ is a terminal vertex of type 2. A terminal vertex of type 2 likewise has no arrows starting from it.

We symbolize the root of an error detection graph by an oval, an ordinary node by a square, a terminal vertex of type 1 by a circle and a terminal vertex of type 2 by a rectangle. The error detection tree G_i has at most $m_0 \cdot m_i$ nodes. All of the predecessor nodes of terminal vertices of type 1 are individually located in the error detection tree G_i. If (z_1, z_2) is the predecessor node of the type 1 terminal vertex $(f(z_1, x), f_i(z_2, x))$, then we set

$$g_c(z_1, (x, g_i(z_2, x))) = 1$$

$$f_c(z_1, (x, g_i(z_2. x))) = - (\text{don't care})$$

where in the automata graph of C an edge marked by $(x, g_i(z_2, x))$, 1 has to be drawn at the state z_1, the end point of which remains free, because the successor state of z_1 is undetermined.

In the same way, all of the error detection graphs $G_1 \cdots G_n$ have to be processed. (Of course, an edge with a given marking is to be entered only once into the graph of C.)

Step 3 After all the error detection trees have been processed in the way described in step 2, we have to set

$$g_c(z, (x, y)) = -(\text{don't care})$$

$$f_c(z, (x, y)) = -(\text{don't care})$$

for all $z \in Z$, $x \in X$ and $y \in Y$ for which the output function and the transition function have not yet been determined after step 1 or step 2. In the automata graph at z we have to enter arrows marked by (x, y), —, whose end points remain free.

For the automaton $A = (X, Z, z_0, f)$ with the error model $F(A)$, the error detection automaton C determined by the described method is equivalent to the automaton D determined by Eqs (3.1) and (3.2) in the case of observable states.

Step 4 The partially defined automaton C with $m = m_0$ states has then to be minimized by one of the common minimizing methods currently implemented on computers for partially defined sequential automata. In cases where the don't-care conditions need not be stated explicitly, in such a method, of course, step 3 can be dropped.

Certain modifications and simplifications for determining optimum error detection circuits are obtained according to the various possible error models. To give some examples, we consider the following cases:

1. At some unknown time T, $T \geqslant 0$, let the automaton A be disturbed to change into the automaton A'. Then the elements of the error model $F(A)$ to be considered would be

$$A_1 = A'$$

$$A_2 = \begin{cases} A & \text{for } t = 0 \\ A' & \text{for } t > 0 \end{cases}$$

$$A_3 = \begin{cases} A & \text{for } t \leqslant 1 \\ A' & \text{for } t > 1 \end{cases}$$

$$\vdots$$

$$A_T = \begin{cases} A & \text{for } t \leqslant T - 2 \\ A' & \text{for } t > T - 2 \end{cases}$$

where T is the operating time of the circuit. Of course this is practically impossible.

In this case one can make use of the fact that, when the failure changing A into A' occurs at any time, the automaton must be in one of its states $z \in Z$, so that it will suffice to set up an error detection tree for (A, A') for all roots (z, z), such that $z \in Z$ and z can be reached from z_0. Evaluation of these, at most $|Z|$, error detection trees ensures that all disturbances changing A into A' which occur at any time $t \geqslant 0$ are taken into account.

The error detection trees for the automata (A, A') with the roots (z, z), $z \in Z$, can be simplified considerably. We specify those nodes of the trees that are not terminal vertices of type 1 and occur in another already established error detection tree with a different root, but not as terminal vertices of type 1 of this tree. They should be treated as terminal vertices of type 2, which are not to be continued. The continuation of such nodes is then described in an already established error detection tree, and hence need not be repeated here.

2. At some unknown time t, $t \geqslant 0$, a transient error $A(t)_i$ occurs, so that the automaton A is disturbed to change into A_i at this time, but operates like A again from the next clock tick onwards. The elements of the error model to be considered would then be

$$A(1)_i = \begin{cases} A_i & \text{for } t = 0 \\ A & \text{for } t \neq 0 \end{cases}$$

$$A(2)_i = \begin{cases} A_i & \text{for } t = 1 \\ A & \text{for } t \neq 1 \end{cases}$$

$$A(3)_i = \begin{cases} A_i & \text{for } t = 2 \\ A & \text{for } t \neq 2 \end{cases}$$

$$\vdots$$

$$A(T' + 1)_i = \begin{cases} A_i & \text{for } t = T' \\ A & \text{for } t \neq T' \end{cases}$$

where again T' is the operating time, of interest, of the circuit. Just as in the case described under 1, it will suffice to set up the error detection trees for $(A, A(1)_i)$ with the roots (z, z) for all states $z \in Z$ that can be reached from z_0.

Also, in this case, the error detection trees for the different roots (z, z) can be simplified by specifying that those nodes of the trees that are not terminal vertices of type 1 and occur as ordinary nodes in an already existing error detection tree should be treated as terminal vertices of type 2, which are not continued.

Generally, of course, there will be several different automata A_i into which the automaton A may change due to a disturbance.

3. Let A be a partially defined sequential automaton. The following variants, for example, are then possible.

   (a) For certain states z' in a subset Z' of Z, the state transition function and the output function are defined only for input values in a set $X_z \subseteq X$, because only values x in X_z are input into the automaton, in a particular state $z' \in Z'$. In the error detection tree G_i for (A, A_i), $A_i \in F(A)$, for a node (z', z) with $z \in Z$, $z' \in Z'$, one then has to consider only successor nodes $(f(z', x), f_i(z, x))$ with $x \in X_z$.

   (b) For certain states z in a subset $Z' \subseteq Z$, the output function g is not defined for certain input values $x \in X_z \subseteq X$, although the transition function is actually defined. An arrow leading from (z', z), $z \in Z$, $z' \in Z'$ to $(f(z', x), f_i(z, x))$, with $x \in X_z$, has then to be marked by x, — and $g_i(z, x)$, and $(f(z, x), f_i(z, x))$ is not a terminal vertex of type 1.

   In the special case where $A = (X, Z, z_0, f)$ and the automata $A_i = (X, Z_i, z_{0i}, f_i)$, $i = 1, \ldots, K$ of the error model, $F(A) = \{A_0 = A, A_1, \ldots, A_K\}$ are half-automata (or automata with observable states) we have the following steps.

Step 1 For $x \in X$, $z, z' \in Z$ we set

$$f_c(z, (x, z')) = z' \qquad \text{for } f(z, x) = z'$$

$$g_c(z, (x, z')) = 0 \qquad \text{for } f(z, x) = z'$$

This means that in the automata graph of A an arrow extending from z to z', being marked by x, is replaced by an arrow marked by (x, z') and 0.

Step 2 Again, for each automaton $A_i \in F(A)$ we determine an error detection tree G_i that describes the difference in behaviour between A and A_i up until the first externally observable error (type 1 vertex). The nodes of the error detection tree are the state pairs (z, z'), $z \in Z$, $z' \in Z_i$. The root of the tree G_i is the pair (z_0, z_{0i}) of the initial states of A and A_i.

For $x \in X$, a node (z, z') of the error detection tree G_i is connected with the node $f(z, x), f_i(z', x)$ by an arrow pointing from (z, z') to $(f(z, x), f_i(z', x))$ which is marked by $x, f(z, x), f(z', x)$. If $f(z, x) \neq f_i(z', x)$ then $f(z, x), f_i(z', x)$ is a terminal vertex of type 1.

If (z, z') with $z \neq z'$ is a node of the error detection tree G_i then (z, z') has to be a terminal vertex of type 1. Therefore, for all predecessor nodes (z_1, z_2) of a terminal vertex of type 1 $f(z_1, x), f_i(z_2, x)$ we have $z_1 = z_2$.

If (z, z) is the predecessor node of the type 1 terminal vertex $f(z, x)$, $f_i(z, x)$, then we set

$$g_c(z, (x, f_i(z, x))) = 1$$

$$f_c(z, (x, f_i(z, x))) = -(\text{don't care})$$

In the automata graph of C an edge marked by $(x, f_i(z, x))$, 1 has to be drawn at the state z, the end point of which remains free, because the successor state of z is determined.

All the error detection trees $G_1, \ldots, G_n$ have, likewise, to be processed.

Step 3 After all the error detection trees have been processed in the way described, we have to set

$$f_c(z, (x, z')) = -\text{(don't care)}$$

$$g_c(z, (x, z')) = -\text{(don't care)}$$

for all $z \in Z$, $z' \in Z_i$, $x \in X$ for which the output function g_c and the next state function f_c have not yet been determined after step 1 and step 2, and in the automata graph of C we have to enter at state z arrows marked by (x, z'), —, whose end points remain free.

For the automaton $A = (X, Z, z_0, f)$ with the error model $F(A)$, the error detection automaton C determined by the described method is equivalent to the automaton D determined by Eqs (3.1) and (3.2) in the case of observable states.

Step 4 The partially defined automaton C has to be minimized as before.

3.5 EXAMPLES

Let us now illustrate the method presented above by a simple example for different error models. The computer aided determination of the corresponding error detection circuit, which is required for practically relevant circuitry, is dealt with in the next section.

Let A_s be a sequential circuit for implementing the automaton $A = (X = \{0,1\}, \ Y = Z = \{00, \ 01, \ 10, \ 11\}, \ z_0 = 00, \ f, \ g)$ with $f = (f_2, \ f_1)$, $g = (g_2, g_1)$ and

$$z_1(t + 1) = f_1(z_2(t), z_1(t), x(t)) = \bar{x}(t) \wedge z_1(t) \vee x(t) \wedge \bar{z}_2(t)$$

$$z_2(t + 1) = f_2(z_2(t), z_1(t), x(t)) = z_1(t)$$

$$y_1(t) = g_1(z_2(t), z_1(t), x(t)) = \bar{z}_1(t)$$

$$y_2(t) = g_2(z_2(t), z_1(t), x(t)) = x(t) \oplus z_2(t)$$

Figure 3.28 shows the automata graph of the automaton A.

As an example of a simple, frequently used functional error model, we suppose here that only single-bit errors, either of the state transition or of the output of the automaton A, may occur. The functional error model $F(A)$ consists of 32 automata

$$A_i = (X, Y, Z, z_0 = 00, f_i, g_i), \qquad i = 1, \ldots, 32$$

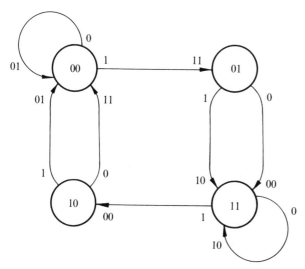

Figure 3.28 Automaton graph of the automaton A.

We assign the first 16 automata $A_1, \ldots, A_{16}$ of the error model to the 16 different considered 1-bit errors of the state transition. Each of the state transition functions $f_1, \ldots, f_{16}$ of the automata $A_1, \ldots, A_{16}$ differ from the state transition function f of A in exactly one value.

The automaton $A_1 = (X, Y, Z, z_0 = 00, f_1, g_1)$ with

$$f_1(z, x) = \begin{cases} 01 & \text{for } z = 00 \text{ and } x = 0 \\ f(z, x) & \text{in all other cases} \end{cases}$$

and

$$g_1 = g$$

is represented in Fig. 3.29. Instead of $f(00, 0) = 00$ for A we have $f_1(00, 0) = 01$ for A_1. It is seen that the states 00 and 01 differ by exactly one bit. This is the only difference between A and A_1. The output functions g and g_1 of A and A_1, respectively, are identical. In an abbreviated form the automaton A_1 will be described by $f_1(00, 0) = 01$, the only value for which f_1 and g_1 of A_1 are different from f and g of A, respectively.

The automaton A_2 is thus described by $f_2(00, 0) = 10$. The corresponding automata graph of A_2 is given in Fig. 3.30.

Analogously, the automata A_3 to A_{16} will be described by

$$f_3(00, 1) = 00, \quad f_4(00, 1) = 11, \quad f_5(01, 0) = 01, \quad f_6(01, 0) = 10$$

$$f_7(01, 1) = 01, \quad f_8(01, 1) = 10, \quad f_9(11, 0) = 01, \quad f_{10}(11, 0) = 10$$

$$f_{11}(11, 1) = 11, \quad f_{12}(11, 1) = 00, \quad f_{13}(10, 0) = 10, \quad f_{14}(10, 0) = 01$$

$$f_{15}(10, 1) = 10, \quad f_{16}(10, 1) = 01$$

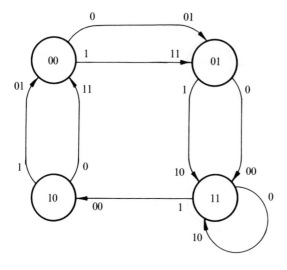

Figure 3.29 Automaton A_1 of the error model.

The automata $A_{17}, \ldots, A_{32}$ of the error model $F(A)$ which are assigned to single-bit errors of the output function g of A are again represented in an abbreviated form. Thus the automaton $A_{17} = (X, Y, Z, z_0, f_{17}, g_{17})$ of Fig. 3.31 with

$$f_{17} = f$$

$$g_{17}(z, x) = \begin{cases} 00 & \text{for } z = 00, x = 0 \\ g(z, x) & \text{otherwise} \end{cases}$$

will be described by $g_{17}(00, 0) = 00$ only.

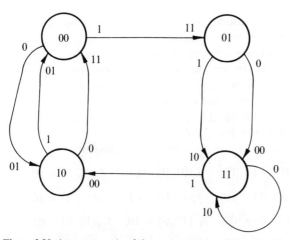

Figure 3.30 Automaton A_2 of the error model.

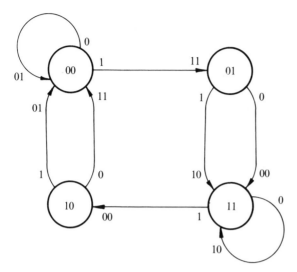

Figure 3.31 Automaton A_{17} of the error model.

Similarly, the automata A_{18} to A_{32} are given by

$g_{18}(00, 0) = 11$, $g_{19}(00, 1) = 10$, $g_{20}(00, 1) = 01$, $g_{21}(01, 0) = 01$

$g_{22}(01, 0) = 10$, $g_{23}(01, 1) = 11$, $g_{24}(01, 1) = 00$, $g_{25}(11, 0) = 11$

$g_{26}(11, 0) = 00$, $g_{27}(11, 1) = 01$, $g_{28}(11, 1) = 10$, $g_{29}(10, 0) = 10$

$g_{30}(10, 0) = 01$, $g_{31}(10, 1) = 00$, $g_{32}(10, 1) = 11$

For all pairs (A, A_i), $i = 1, \ldots, 32$, we have to set up the error detection trees as described. As pointed out previously, the root of a tree is represented by an oval, a type 1 terminal vertex by a circle, a type 2 terminal vertex by a rectangle and an ordinary node by a square.

First of all, we shall explain in detail how the error detecting tree G_1 of Fig. 3.32, assigned to the pair (A, A_1), is established. For the monotony of the description of G_1, we apologize to the reader in advance. One should follow this description only until one has actually understood the principle.

The root of G_1 is $(00, 00)$ because the initial state of both A and A_1 is the state 00. As a root, $(00, 00)$ is represented by an oval surround. Upon input 0, A as well A_1 output the value $g(00, 0) = g_1(00, 0) = 01$. A passes to the state $f(00, 0) = 00$, whereas A_1 passes to $f_1(00, 0) = 01$. Accordingly, an arrow marked by 0, 01, 01 leads from the root $(00, 00)$ to the ordinary node $(00, 01)$ which is surrounded by a square. Since we have $f(00, 0) = 00$, $f_1(01, 0) = 11$ and $g(00, 0) = 01 \neq 00 = f_1(01, 0)$, an arrow marked by 0, 01, 00 leads from the ordinary node $(00, 01)$ to the type 1 terminal vertex 00, 11 which is surrounded by a circle.

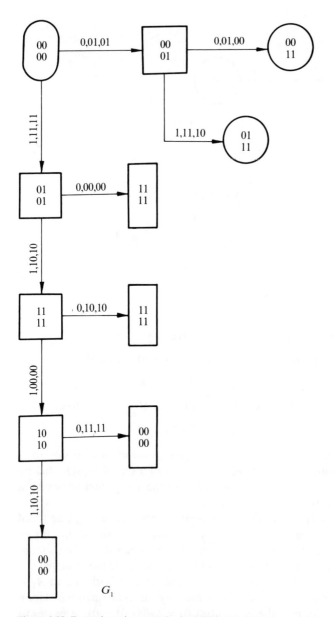

Figure 3.32 Error detection tree G_1 describing the differences in the behaviours of A and A_1.

Because of $f(00, 1) = 01, f_1(01, 1) = 11$ and $g(00, 1) = 11 \neq 10 = g_1(00, 1)$, an arrow labelled with 1, 11, 10 leads from the ordinary node 00, 01 to the type 1 terminal vertex 01, 11. Upon input of 1 in state 00 the automaton A as well as the automaton A_1 pass to state 01 outputting 11 ($f(00, 1) = f_2(00, 1) = 01$, $g(00, 1) = g_1(00, 1) = 11$).

Accordingly, in the error detecting tree G_1 an arrow marked by 1, 11, 11 leads from the node 00, 00 to the node 01, 01, the latter being represented as a square because it is an ordinary node of G_1. When 1 is input in the state 01 the automaton A as well as A_1 pass into state 11, outputting 10. An arrow labelled with 1, 10, 10 leads from the ordinary node (01, 10) to the ordinary node (11, 11). When 0 is input in state 01 the automaton A as well as A_1 pass into state 11, outputting 00.

Thus, an arrow marked with 0, 00, 00 leads from node (01, 01) to a node (11, 11). Because a node (11, 11) has already occurred, this node is made a type 2 terminal vertex, represented by a rectangle. Since $f(11, 0) = f_1(11, 0) = 11$, $g(11, 0) = g_1(11, 0) = 10$, in G_1 there is an edge marked by 0, 10, 10 which leads from the ordinary node 11, 11 to a second type 2 terminal node 11, 11. Since $f(11, 1) = f_1(11, 1) = 10$ and $g(11, 1) = g_1(11, 1) = 00$ in G_1 there is an edge marked with 1, 00, 00 which leads from the ordinary node 11, 11 to the ordinary node 10, 10.

Since $f(10, 0) = f_1(10, 0) = 00$ and $g(10, 0) = g_1(10, 0) = 11$, in G_1 there is an edge marked with 0, 11, 11 which leads from the ordinary node 10, 10 to the node 00, 00, the latter being a type 2 terminal vertex, because a node 00, 00 has already occurred as the root of G_1. Since $f(10, 1) = f_1(10, 1) = 00$ and $g(10, 1) = g_1(10, 1) = 01$, in G_1 there is an edge marked by 1, 01, 01 leading from the ordinary node 10, 10 to the type 2 terminal vertex 00, 00. Thus G_1 has been completely determined.

The error detection tree G_1 describes the first appearance of a difference in the behaviour of A and A_1 by type 1 terminal vertices, in the present case by the nodes (00, 11) and (01, 11), respectively. For an arbitrary input sequence it is possible to trace, by means of the error detecting tree, when the supposed error in A causing it to change into A_1 will affect the output for the first time. If we consider, for example, the input sequence 101000... then A and A_1 pass through the states (00, 00), (01, 01), (11, 11), (10, 10), (00, 00), (00, 01), (00, 11), corresponding to the nodes of G_1 until a type 1 terminal vertex, (00, 11), is reached.

Although the automata A and A_1 are in different states 00, 01, after the input of 10100 the output is only affected when the next input symbol 0 is inputted and when the type 1 terminal vertex (00, 11) is reached. (If a type 2 terminal in the tree is reached, here (11, 11) or (00, 00), then the run is continued from the respective ordinary node with the same marking.) Upon arrival at a type 1 terminal vertex the supposed error becomes externally detectable.

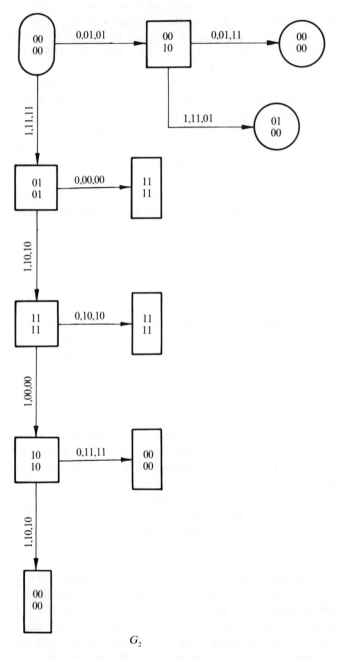

Figure 3.33 Error detection tree G_2 describing the differences in the behaviours of A and A_2.

The error detecting trees $G_2, G_3, \ldots, G_{32}$ are determined in precisely the same way as described in the procedure above. Figure 3.33 shows the error detecting tree G_2. The error detecting trees G_3, G_4 and G_{14} are given in Figs 3.34 and 3.35, respectively, while the error detecting trees G_{17} and G_{32} are represented in Figs 3.36 and 3.37. It is left as an exercise for the reader to draw the other error detecting trees for the error model $F(A)$.

By modifying the standard automaton $A_0 = A$ we now determine the partially defined automaton C, which has the same number of states as A, equivalent to the error detecting automaton B. Executing step 1 as described previously, in the automata graph of A we substitute an arrow marked by (x, y), 0 for an arrow leading from z to z', which is marked by x and y, as shown in Fig. 3.38. This ensures that no error is indicated when the circuit to be monitored does actually behave correctly.

For the further determination of C we now locate all the predecessor nodes of type 1 terminal vertices in the error detection trees $G_1, \ldots, G_{32}$. If (z_1, z_2) is a predecessor node of the type 1 terminal vertex $f(z_1, x), f_i(z_2, x)$, then in the automata graph of C, at state z_1, we draw an edge marked by $(x, g_i(z_2, x))$, 1, whose end point remains free.

The error detection tree G_1 has the two type 1 terminal vertices $(00, 11)$ and $(01, 11)$. The predecessor node of $(00, 11)$ with $f(00, 0) = 00$ and

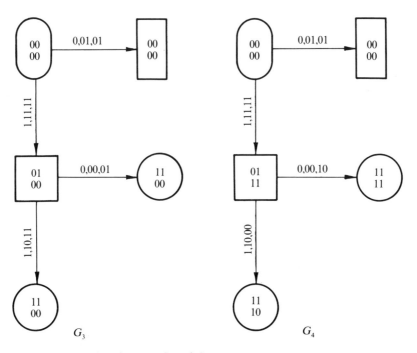

Figure 3.34 Error detection trees G_3 and G_4.

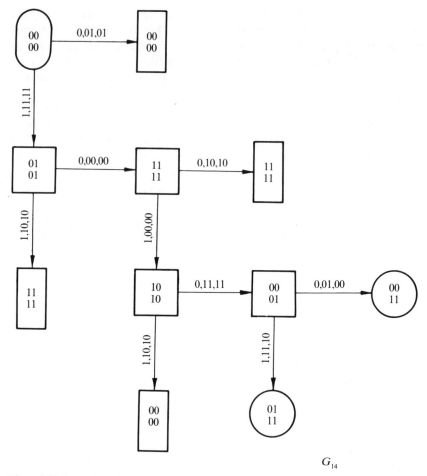

Figure 3.35 Error detection tree G_{14}.

$f_1(01, 0) = 11$ is the node $(00, 01)$. Therefore, in the automata graph of C at state 00, one has to draw an edge, marked by $((0, g_1(01, 0)), 1) = ((0, 00), 1)$, whose end point remains free (don't care).

The predecessor node of $(01, 11)$ with $f(00, 1) = 01$, $f_1(01, 1) = 11$ is also the node $(00, 01)$. Therefore, in the automata graph of C at state 00, one has to draw an edge marked by $((1, g_1(01, 1)), 1) = ((1, 10), 1)$, whose end point remains free.

These modifications are represented in Fig. 3.39. The automaton of Fig. 3.39 detects the error A disturbed into A_1. In a similar way the edges marked by $(0, 11)$, 1 and $(1, 01)$, 1 starting from the state 00 of C, with free end points, are obtained from the error detection tree G_2.

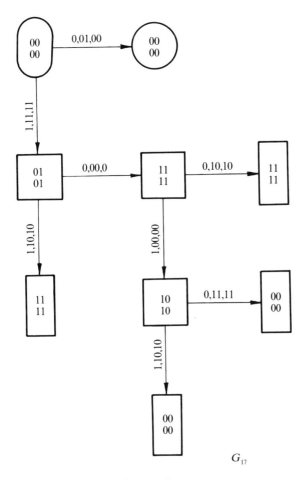

Figure 3.36 Error detection tree G_{17}.

Figure 3.40 shows the graph of the automaton C in which all the error detection trees $G_1, \ldots, G_{32}$ have been taken into account. All of the arrows of the automata graph of C for which both the output and the next state are not determined (don't care) are omitted in Fig. 3.40. Thus, for example, the arrow starting from state 00 and marked with $(0, 10)$, —, whose end point remains free, is omitted.

It is of interest to mention here that different error detection trees may result in the same arrows of the error detecting automaton C. Thus, both the error detection trees G_1 and G_{14} represented in Figs 3.32 and 3.35, respectively, give rise to the arrows starting in state 00 and marked with $(0, 00)$, 1 and $(1, 10)$, 1, although the corresponding automata of the error

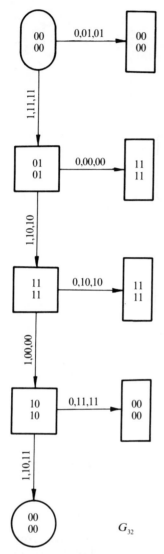

Figure 3.37 Error detection tree G_{32}.

model A_1 and A_{14} are different. The arrow marked with $(0, 00)$, 1 is also determined by the error detecting tree G_{17}.

Like the standard automaton A, the automaton $C = (X \times Y, \{0, 1\}, Z, f_c, g_c)$ has only four states. Table 3.5 shows the functions f_c and g_c. The error detection automaton B whose implementation is the desired error detecting circuit is obtained from C by state reduction. Since the states 00 and 11 and 01 and 10 are compatible they are combined into compatibility classes,

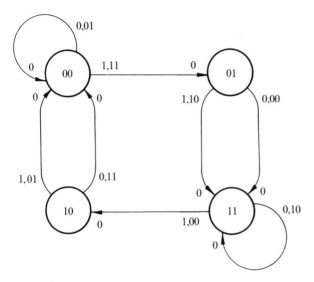

Figure 3.38 First step of the modification of the automaton *A* into the error detection automaton *B*.

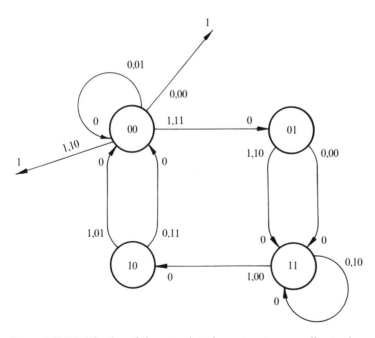

Figure 3.39 Modification of the error detection automaton according to the error detection tree G_1.

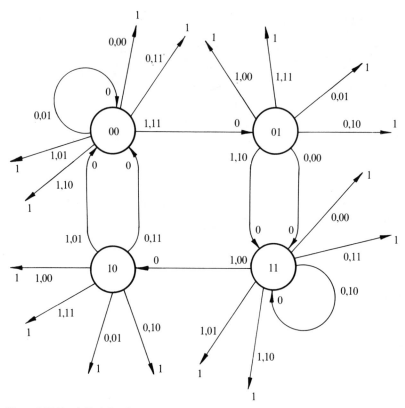

Figure 3.40 Partially defined error detection automaton after the processing of all error detection trees.

$A = \{00, 11\}$ and $B = \{01, 10\}$. For $\boldsymbol{B} = (X \times Y, \{0, 1\}, \{A, B\}, f_B g_B)$ the representation of f_B and g_B given in Table 3.6 is then obtained from Table 3.5. The error detection automaton is shown in Fig. 3.41.

If we encode $A = 1$, $B = 0$, $y = y_2$, y_1 the state transition function f_B of $\boldsymbol{B}$ may be determined as

$$f_B(z, x, y_2, y_1) = \overline{z \wedge x} = \bar{z} \vee \bar{x}$$

For the output function g_B we have

$$g_B(z, x, y_2, y_1) = z \oplus x \oplus y_2 \oplus y_1$$

The error detection automaton has only two states whereas the automaton A to be monitored has four states.

In comparison with the approach described above, it is of interest to point out that the construction of the error detection circuit from the 33 automata $A, A_1, \ldots, A_{32}$ with four states, each according to Fig. 3.27, first

Table 3.5

z	x	y	$f_{\mathrm{e}}(z, x, y)$	$g_{\mathrm{e}}(z, x, y)$
00	0	00	—	1
	0	01	00	0
	0	10	—	—
	0	11	—	1
	1	00	—	—
	1	01	—	1
	1	10	—	1
	1	11	01	0
01	0	00	11	0
	0	01	—	1
	0	10	—	1
	0	11	—	—
	1	00	—	1
	1	01	—	—
	1	10	11	0
	1	11	—	1
10	0	00	—	—
	0	01	—	1
	0	10	—	1
	0	11	00	0
	1	00	—	1
	1	01	00	0
	1	10	—	—
	1	11	—	1
11	0	00	—	1
	0	01	—	—
	0	10	11	0
	0	11	—	1
	1	00	10	0
	1	01	—	1
	1	10	—	1
	1	11	—	—

led to an automaton with 2^{67} states whose direct state reduction by generally known methods is absolutely hopeless, even in such a simple case. In the example just considered, we had assumed that the circuit A_{s} from the very beginning implements A or, in the case of an error, $A_1, \ldots, A_{32}$. Now we assume that from any time T onwards the circuit A_{s} may implement one of the 32 automata $A_1, \ldots, A_{32}$ instead of the automaton A.

Up to time T, A_{s} implements the automaton A. Since at the time of occurrence of the error 'one of the automata A_i is implemented instead of A from time T on', the circuit A_{s} may be in any of its states $z \in Z$. This means that for each pair (A, A_i), $i = 1, \ldots, 32$, one has to establish the error

Table 3.6

z	x	y	$f_B(z, x, y)$	$g_B(z, x, y)$
A	0	00	—	1
	0	01	A	0
	0	10	A	0
	0	11	—	1
	1	00	B	0
	1	01	—	1
	1	10	—	1
	1	11	B	0
B	0	00	A	0
	0	01	—	1
	0	10	—	1
	0	11	A	0
	1	00	—	1
	1	01	A	0
	1	10	A	0
	1	11	—	1

detection tree for all roots (z, z) with $z \in \{00, 01, 10, 11\}$. Thus we have to consider $4 \times 32 = 128$ error detection trees which can, however, as we shall show, be simplified considerably.

For the pair of automata (A, A_i) we denote the error detection tree with the root (z, z) by $G_i(z)$ and the set of type 1 terminal vertices of $G_i(z)$ by $T_{1i}(z)$. The following theorem, which is obvious from the construction of the

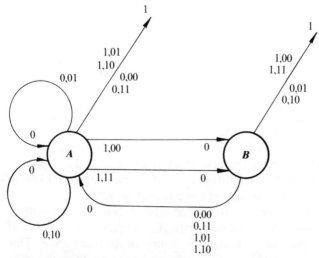

Figure 3.41 Optimized error detection automaton.

error detection trees, simplified the determination of all type 1 terminal vertices for a given pair of automata.

Let $G_i(z)$ be an error detection tree of the pair (A, A_i) of automata and let $T_{1i}(z)$ be the set of type 1 terminal vertices of $G_i(z)$. If (z', z') is an ordinary node of $G_i(z)$ then the set $T_{1i}(z')$ of type 1 terminal vertices of $G_i(z')$ is contained in $T_{1i}(z)$:

$$T_{1i}(z') \subseteq T_{1i}(z)$$

An example of the application of this theorem is as follows. In Fig. 3.32 the error detection tree $G_1 = G_1(00)$ is shown. The error detection trees $G_1(01)$, $G_1(10)$ and $G_1(11)$ are shown in Figs 3.42 and 3.43. For the type 1 terminal vertices we have $T_{11}(00) = T_{11}(01) = T_{11}(10) = T_{11}(11)$, which follows for $z \in Z$ by inspection of $G_1(z)$. Because $(01, 01), (10, 10)$ and $(11, 11)$ are ordinary nodes of $G_1(00)$ it follows that we have

$$T_{11}(z) \subseteq T_{11}(00) \qquad \text{for } z \in \{01, 10, 11\}$$

and the error detection trees did not have to be investigated in detail.

As a next example we consider the determination of all of the type 1 terminal vertices of $G_3(z)$, $z \in \{00, 01, 10, 11\}$. $G_3 = G_3(00)$ with $T_{13}(00) = \{(11, 00), (11, 00)\}$ is shown in Fig. 3.34. None of the nodes (z, z) with $z \in \{01, 10, 11\}$ is an ordinary node of $G_3(00)$. However, $G_3(01)$ of Fig. 3.43 with

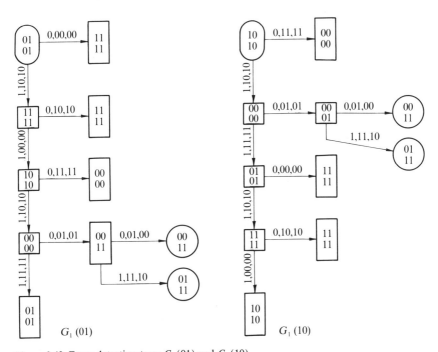

Figure 3.42 Error detection trees $G_1(01)$ and $G_1(10)$.

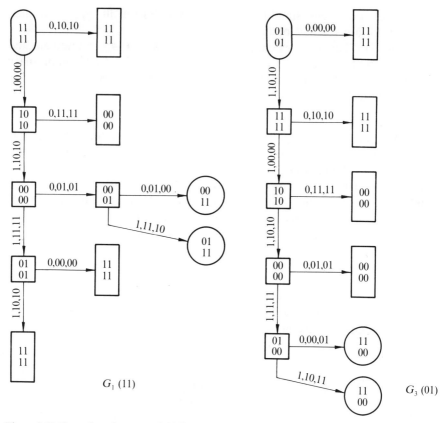

Figure 3.43 Error detection trees $G_1(11)$ and $G_3(01)$.

$T_{13}(01) = T_{13}(00)$ contains the nodes $(10, 10)$ and $(11, 11)$ as ordinary nodes, from which we conclude

$$T_{13}(10) = T_{13}(11) = T_{13}(01) = T_{13}(00)$$

In the same way, it is possible to show that no new type 1 terminal vertices will be generated by all error detection trees $G_i(z)$, $i = 1, \ldots, 32$, $z \in \{01, 10, 11\}$. This gives the same solution for the error-detecting automaton as in the previous example.

In the following example we assume that at any time in the circuit A_s a transient failure may occur, changing it into one of the automata $A_1, \ldots, A_{32}$ for a single cycle of time. Otherwise A_s is assumed to implement the automaton A.

At the time when a transient failure may occur, the monitored automaton A may be in an arbitrary state. Therefore we need to establish the error detection trees with the root (z, z) for all $z \in \{00, 01, 10, 11\}$ and for all pairs

$(A, A_i(t))$, $i = 1, \ldots, 32$, with

$$A_i(t) = (X, Y, Z, f^t_i, g^t_i)$$

and

$$f^t_i = \begin{cases} f_i & \text{for } t = 0 \\ f & \text{for } t > 0 \end{cases}$$

$$g^t_i = \begin{cases} g_i & \text{for } t = 0 \\ g & \text{for } t > 0 \end{cases}$$

As an example we consider the error detection trees for $(A, A_{11}(t))$. In its abbreviated form, the automaton A_{11} can be characterized by $f_{11}(11, 1) = 11$. Inputting $x = 1$ in state 11 the automaton A_{11} remains in state 11 whereas the automaton A is transferred into state 10. For $t = 0$, the automata $A_{11}(t)$ and A_{11} coincide; for $t > 0$, $A_{11}(t)$ and A are identical. The state diagrams of A_{11} and $A_{11}(t)$ are shown in Fig. 3.44.

Since, for $t > 0$, $A_{11}(t)$ and A are identical, the error detection trees $G_{11}(t, z)$ with $z \in \{00, 01, 10\}$ have only type 2 terminal nodes, which do not contribute to the error detection automaton. The essential part of the error detection trees $G_{11}(t, 11)$ and $G_{11}(11)$ are shown in Fig. 3.45. Although the set of type 1 terminal nodes of $G_{11}(t, 11)$ and $G_{11}(11)$ are different, the predecessors of the corresponding type 1 terminal nodes are identical.

In the process of modification of the automaton A into C, the same edge marked by 0, 10, 1 and 1, 00, 1 with a free end point have to be added at state 10 of C for both $G_{11}(11)$ and $G_{11}(t, 11)$. In an analogous way it can be verified that for all other i and z, the error detection trees $G_i(t, z)$ for the

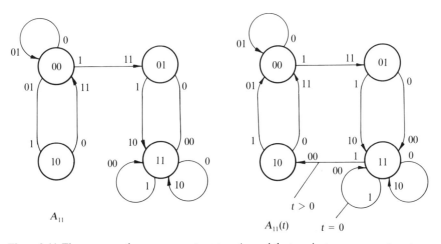

A_{11}

$A_{11}(t)$ $t = 0$ $t > 0$

Figure 3.44 The permanently erroneous automaton A_{11} and the transient erroneous automaton $A_{11}(t)$.

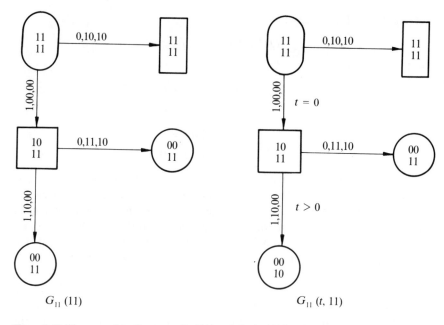

Figure 3.45 The error detection trees $G_{11}(11)$ and $G_{11}(t, 11)$ for the corresponding permanent and transient errors.

pairs $(A, A_i(t))$ give rise to the same modifications of A into C as the error detection trees $G_i(z)$ for the pairs (A, A_i). Therefore, one obtains the same error detection automaton as in the two preceding examples.

3.6 REDUCTION OF OVERHEAD BY RESTRICTED ERROR MODEL AND REDUCED ERROR DETECTION

Here we investigate the problem of how to determine error detection circuits that are sufficiently simple for sequential circuits by selective reduction of the error model.

If the expenditure required to implement the error-detecting automaton B for an automaton A with the error model $F(A)$ is too high, this suggests first of all that an error-detecting automaton B' with a reduced error model $F'(A) \subset F(A)$ should be determined. Since $F'(A)$ is a subset of $F(A)$, the expenditure required for the implementation of B' is at most equal to that required to implement B. In concrete terms, the point is to select a subset $F'(A)$ of $F(A)$ such that B' becomes as simple as possible, while $F'(A)$ differs as little as possible from $F(A)$.

Apart from the systematic trial-and-error method, a general efficient method for a suitable selection of $F'(A)$ is now known. For example, frequently a suitable selection can be made by simply eliminating automata from the error model in such a way that different states of the automaton B can be merged. Another important possibility of reducing the overhead required for error detection (with the error model remaining unchanged) is to allow an error not to be detected, with certainty, at the time of its first effect on the output, but possibly at a later time.

For this case there are several reasonable requirements that can be placed on delayed error detection. If A is disturbed to change into A_i and if the error detection circuit A_s does not detect the error upon input of px, $p \in X^*$, $x \in X$, although $g(z_0, px) \neq g_i(z_{0i}, px)$, and $g(z_0, p) = g_i(z_0, p)$, then we require either of the following:

1. For any input word $p_1 \in X^*$ upon whose input subsequent to p the error considered is still not detected by B_s, there exists a third input word $p_2 \in X^*$ such that the error 'A disturbed to change into A_i' is detected by B_s upon input of pxp_1p_2.
2. There exists an input word p' such that the error 'A disturbed to change into A_i' is detected by B_s upon input of pxp'.

In the first case the information about an error is not lost, at least up to its first indication. If it has not already been indicated, it can always be detected by inputing a suitable word. This may be due to the fact that the error continues to exist as a hardware failure or to the specific kind of state transfer of the error-detecting automaton. In the second case the information about, say, a transient error may be lost. However, for every error there exists an input word that causes its detection.

We may accomplish the modification of B into B' with a reduced error-detecting capability by using the error detection trees G_i of (A, A_i). We continue the error detection tree G_i at type 1 terminal vertices until we arrive at type 2 terminal vertices or new type 1 terminal vertices. (If the states of a considered type 1 terminal vertex are identical the error detection tree has not to be continued at this type 1 terminal vertex.)

When the first requirement is satisfied, we can ignore an original type 1 terminal vertex in modifying A into C' iff from all of its successor nodes there exists a path to another type 1 terminal vertex. Here a path through a type 2 terminal vertex has to be continued in the corresponding ordinary node of the error detecting tree with the same marking.

New type 1 terminal vertices are to be taken into account in the modification of A into C' if they can be reached from an ignored type 1 terminal vertex. In the case of the second requirement a type 1 terminal vertex can be ignored if there exists a path from it to another type 1 terminal vertex.

The different approaches to the reduction of the error model as described above will now be illustrated by simple examples.

3.6.1 Reduced Error Model

Starting from the automaton shown in Fig. 3.3 and the automata $A_1, \ldots, A_{16}$ shown in Fig. 3.4, we obtained the partially defined (unreduced) error detection automaton of Fig. 3.7, which can be reduced to an error detection automaton with two states whose transition function and output function are shown in Table 3.3. The aim of the reduction of the error model is to simplify the automaton D_{min}. Since D_{min} has two states, the error model $F(A) = (A_1, \ldots, A_{16})$ has to be restricted in such a way that D_{min} can be replaced by a combinational error-detecting circuit K (with only one state). The error model $F(A)$ must then be reduced to $F^*(A) \subset F(A)$ in such a way that the two states A and B become compatible and can be merged. The combinational circuit K must not indicate any error if the circuit A_s implements the standard automaton A correctly.

Those rows in Table 3.4 where the output function $gD_{min}(z, x, z')$ is zero correspond to a correct operation of A_s. In particular, one has

$$gD_{min}(A, 0, 00) = gD_{min}(A, 0, 11) = gD_{min}(A, 1, 01) = 0$$

$$gD_{min}(A, 1, 10) = gD_{min}(B, 0, 00) = gD_{min}(B, 1, 00) = 0$$

If A and B are to be merged into a single state, so that D can be replaced by a combinational circuit K, then one obtains

$$K(0, 00) = K(0, 11) = K(1, 00) = K(1, 01) = K(1, 10) = 0$$

This assumption guarantees that no error is indicated as long as A_s operates correctly.

If we have $gD_{min}(z, x, z') = 0$ for some $z, z' \in Z$ and therefore $K(x, z') = 0$ then for $A_i \in F(A)$ it is impossible to detect an erroneous state transition $f_i(z, x) = z' \neq f(z, x)$. In the considered example we have

$$K(1, 00) = 0$$

but

$$f_4(00, 1) = 00 \neq f(00, 1) = 01$$

$$f_6(01, 1) = 00 \neq f(01, 1) = 01$$

$$f_{11}(11, 1) = 00 \neq f(11, 1) = 10$$

$$K(1, 01) = 0$$

but

$$f_{15}(10, 1) = 01 \neq f(10, 1) = 00$$

and

$$K(1, 10) = 0$$

but

$$f_{16}(10, 1) = 10 \neq f(10, 1) = 00$$

and the combinational error detection circuit K can not detect the errors A changed into A_4, A_6, A_{11}, A_{15} and A_{16}.

However, if we set $F^*(A) = \{A_0, A_1, A_2, A_3, A_5, A_7, A_8, A_9, A_{10}, A_{12}, A_{13}, A_{14}\} \subseteq F(A)$ then for this restricted error model we obtain the error detecting automaton D^* described in Table 3.7. The states 00, 01, 10, 11 are all compatible with one another and can be merged to one state, so that the

Table 3.7

z	x	y	$fD_{min}(z, x, z')$	$gD_{min}(z, x, z')$	$A_i \in F^*(A)$
00	0	00	00	0	A
00	0	01	—	1	A_1
00	0	10	—	1	A_2
00	0	11	—	—	—
00	1	00	—	—	—
00	1	01	01	0	A
00	1	10	—	—	—
00	1	11	—	1	A_3
01	0	00	—	—	—
01	0	01	—	1	A_8
01	0	10	—	1	A_7
01	0	11	11	0	A
01	1	00	—	—	—
01	1	01	01	0	A
01	1	10	—	—	—
01	1	11	—	1	A_5
10	0	00	00	0	A
10	0	01	—	1	A_{14}
10	0	10	—	1	A_{13}
10	0	11	—	—	—
10	1	00	00	0	A
10	1	01	—	—	—
10	1	10	—	—	—
10	1	11	—	—	—
11	0	00	—	—	—
11	0	01	—	1	A_{10}
11	0	10	—	1	A_9
11	0	11	11	0	A
11	1	00	—	—	—
11	1	01	—	—	—
11	1	10	10	0	A
11	1	11	—	1	A_{12}

Table 3.8

x	z'	$K(xz')$
0	00	0
0	01	1
0	10	1
0	11	0
1	00	0
1	01	0
1	10	0
1	11	1

reduced form of D^* is a combinational circuit K with the input/output behaviour shown in Table 3.8. The combinational circuit K still detects 11 out of 16 errors, i.e. about 70 per cent of the arrows, immediately upon their first effect on the input/output behaviour.

3.6.2 Delayed Error Detection

To illustrate the delayed error detection by a simple example, we again consider the automaton of Fig. 3.3, but now with the error model $F'(A) = \{A_1, \ldots, A_{16}, A_{17}\}$, where $A_1, \ldots, A_{16}$ are the automata of Fig. 3.4 and the automaton A_{17} is shown in Fig. 3.46. Figure 3.47 represents the error detection tree G_{17} for (A, A_{17}).

The (unreduced) error detection automaton D' for the error model $F'(A)$ differs from the error detection automaton D for the error model $F(A)$ of

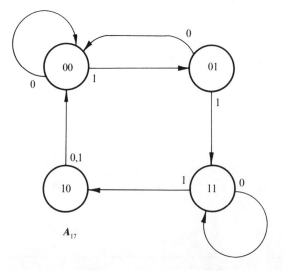

Figure 3.46 Erroneous automaton A_{17}.

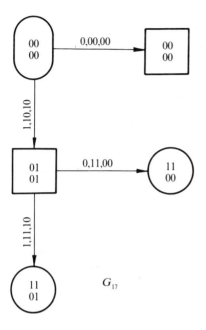

Figure 3.47 Error detection tree G_{17}.

Table 3.9

z	x	z'	$f_{D'*}(z, xz')$	$g_{D'*}(z, xz')$
A	0	00	A	0
A	0	01	—	1
A	0	10	—	1
A	0	11	—	—
A	1	00	—	1
A	1	01	C	0
A	1	10	—	—
A	1	11	—	1
B	0	00	A	0
B	0	01	—	1
B	0	10	—	1
B	0	11	—	—
B	1	00	A	0
B	1	01	—	1
B	1	10	—	1
C	0	00	—	1
C	0	01	—	1
C	0	10	—	1
C	0	11	C	0
C	1	00	—	1
C	1	01	—	0
C	1	10	B	0
C	1	11	—	1

Table 3.5 in that $g_D'(1, 00) = 1$ holds instead of $g_D(1, 00) = —$. However, because of $g_D(0, 00) = g_D'(0, 00) = 0$, the states 00 and 01 are no longer compatible, and D^* has three compatibility classes of states, so that the reduced form D'_{min} of D' has three states. If we set $A = \{00\}$, $B = \{10\}$, $C = \{01, 11\}$, then D'_{min} is obtained as shown in Table 3.9.

By a delayed detection of the error 'A disturbed to change into A_{17}', it is possible to replace the error detection automaton D'_{min} with three states by the error detection automaton D_d (d-delayed) with only two states. To determine D_d, we continue the error detection tree G_{17} at the type 1 terminal vertex (11, 00) through the node (10, 01) to the type 1 terminal vertex (00, 11), as shown in Fig. 3.48. The nodes (11, 00) and (10, 01) are treated as ordinary nodes, being ignored as type 1 terminal vertices.

For every successor node of a type 1 terminal vertex there obviously exists a path to another type 1 terminal vertex. For the unreduced error detection automaton D_d one has $gD_d(10, 1, 11) = 1$, $gD_d(11, 1, 01) = —$ and $gD_d(01, 0, 00) = —$ instead of $gD'(01, 0, 00) = 1$. Otherwise $g_{D'}$ and gD_d coincide. Like the automaton D_{min}, the reduced error-detecting automaton $D_{d\,min}$ described in Table 3.10 has only two states. It differs from D_{min} only

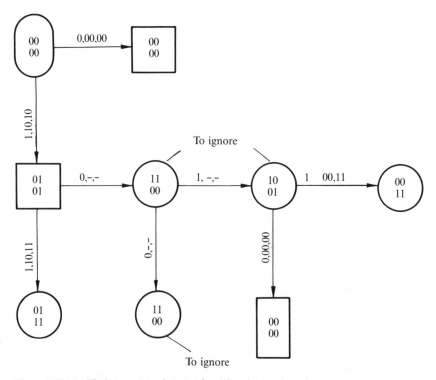

Figure 3.48 Modified error detection tree for delayed error detection.

Table 3.10

z	x	z'	$fD_{\text{d min}}(z, xz')$	$gD_{\text{d min}}(z, x, z')$
A	0	00	A	0
A	0	01	—	1
A	0	10	—	1
A	0	11	A	0
A	1	00	—	1
A	1	01	A	0
A	1	10	B	0
A	1	11	—	1
B	0	00	A	0
B	0	01	—	1
B	0	10	—	1
B	0	11	—	—
B	1	00	A	0
B	1	01	—	1
B	1	10	—	1
B	1	11	—	1

by $gD_{\text{d min}}(B, 1, 11) = 1 \neq gD_{\min}(B, 1, 11) =$ —. The error-detecting automaton $D_{\text{d min}}$ detects the 16 errors of the error model $F(A)$ immediately and the error 'A disturbed to change into A_{17}' with a delay.

3.7 ERROR DETECTION OF ARBITRARY SINGLE FAILURES

In Aksenova and Sogomonyan (1971, 1975), the method developed in Sogomonyan (1970) for combinational circuits is transferred to sequential circuits. In this case the error detection circuit is so designed that all single failures of the sequential circuit to be monitored are detected immediately, even if they have affected only the state transition in the circuit to be monitored, but not yet the output.

The basic difference from the combinational case results from the fact that sequential circuits contain feedback and that the relation R, 'BRB' iff there is a connection from B to B'', which is defined on the set M_B of the components by their connections, is not a partial ordering. It is also clear that failures in the state transition do not necessarily affect the output immediately, but may do so only after some time.

The method for determining maximal classes of components is modified as in the combinational case. Feedback loops disturbing the determination of classes are removed. In this case it is accepted that the determination of classes is no longer unique and that classes are combined in a second step.

The outputs of each class of components are replaced by modified components one after the other. In addition, all storage elements that are not outputs of a class are also replaced by storage elements modified by inverting their outputs, in order that every single failure of state transition be detected immediately.

From the considered automaton A, the modified automata A_i^m, $i = 1, 2, 3, \ldots$, are derived one after the other by carrying out the modifications just described. By means of the automata A, A_1^m, A_2^m, $\ldots$, the automaton table of the error detection circuit is derived, where the successors of each state once encountered in any of the automata A, A_1^m, A_2^m, $\ldots$ are taken into consideration in each of these automata. After detecting the first error, the error detection automaton does not behave arbitrarily, but detects all the single errors that continue to occur. The automata A_i^m, $i = 1, 2, \ldots$, are not those of the error model in the sense of this book, which is immediately clear for transient errors.

A fail-safe design of the error detection automaton is given in Aksenova and Sogomonyan (1975). In the case of a single binary output one obtains duplication and comparison as in the combinational case (for fail-safe design this is an expenditure exceeding that of duplication and comparison). The advantage of detecting all single errors in a relatively compact way and of achieving very good error detection properties is opposed by the disadvantages of (a) a lack of graduated adaptability to more specific failure assumptions and (b) a comparatively very high hardware overhead. Here the overhead is in part also due to the heuristic character of the method. For details we refer readers to the quoted literature.

3.8 LIMITS OF OVERHEAD

So far we have dealt with determining sequential circuits and optimizing error detection circuits with respect to the overhead for a known error model. According to the theory described in this book, our error detection circuit can be easily adapted to the error model under consideration. The error detection circuit detects all the errors of the error model and all the don't-care conditions can be utilized to optimize the error detection circuit. If an error model is not known, then all deviations from the correct behaviour of the monitored circuit have to be detected.

For this case we show that the error detection automaton has to be at best as complex as the monitored automaton. Since the number of states of an automaton may be considered as an estimation of its complexity, we prove at first the following theorem (cf. Meyer and Sunderstrom, 1975) concerning the number of states of the error detection automaton.

Let $A = (X, Y, Z = \{z_1, \ldots, z_n\}, z_0, f, g)$ be a finite reduced automaton with n states which is connected from z_0 and let $B = (X \times Y, \{0, 1\}, Z, z_{0B},$

f_B, g_B) be an error-detecting automaton of A, such that Eq. (3.12) holds true. Then B has at least n pair-wise non-equivalent states.

PROOF Since A is connected from $z_0 \in Z$, for every state $z_i \in Z$ there exists a word $p_i \in X^*$ such that

$$z_i = f(z_0, p_i) \tag{3.16}$$

For $z_i \neq z_j$ one has $p_i \neq p_j$. We denote $q_i = g^*(z_0, p_i)$ with $q_i \in Y^*$.

Since A is reduced by assumption, for any $z_i, z_j \in Z, i \neq j$, there exists an input word $r \in X^*$ such that

$$g^*(z_i, r) \neq g^*(z_j, r) \tag{3.17}$$

is satisfied.

Let r be a shortest word for which Eq. (3.17) holds true. Then there exist elements $y, \tilde{y} \in Y$, with $y \neq \tilde{y}$ and $s \in Y^*$, such that

$$g^*(z_i, r) = sy \quad \text{and} \quad g^*(z_j, r) = s\tilde{y}, \quad r = x_1^r \cdots x_m^r, s = y_1^s \cdots y_{m-1}^s \, (m > 0)$$

Denoting $p_i = x_1^i \cdots x_{ni}^i$, $q_i = y_1^i \cdots y_{ni}^i$, for $i = 1, \ldots, n$, we set

$$z_i' = f_B(z_{0B}, x_1^i y_1^i \cdots x_{ni}^i y_{ni}^i) \tag{3.18}$$

and show that z_i' and z_j' are not equivalent for $i \neq j$. According to Eq. (3.12) one has

$$g_B^*(z_{0B}, x_1^i y_1^i \cdots x_{ni}^i y_{ni}^i x_1^r y_1^s \cdots x_{m-1}^r y_{m-1}^s x_m^r v) = \begin{cases} \underbrace{0 \cdots 0}_{n_i + m} & \text{for } v = y \\ \underbrace{0 \cdots 01}_{n_i + m - 1} & \text{for } v = \tilde{y} \end{cases}$$

$$\tag{3.19}$$

and hence

$$g_B^*(z_i', x_1^r y_1^r \cdots x_m^r y) = \underbrace{0 \cdots 0}_{m}$$

$$g_B^*(z_i', x_1^r y_1^r \cdots x_m^r \tilde{y}) = \underbrace{0 \cdots 01}_{m-1}$$

$$\tag{3.20}$$

and

$$g_B^*(z_{0B}, x_1^j y_1^j \cdots x_{nj}^j y_{nj}^j x_1^r y_1^s \cdots x_{m-1}^r y_{m-1}^s x_m^r u) = \begin{cases} \underbrace{0 \cdots 01}_{n_j + m - 1} & \text{for } u = y \\ \underbrace{0 \cdots 0}_{n_j + m} & \text{for } u = \tilde{y} \end{cases}$$

$$\tag{3.21}$$

which gives

$$g_B^*(z_j', x_1^r y_1^s \cdots x_m^r y) = \underbrace{0 \cdots 0}_{m-1} 1$$

$$g_B^*(z_j', x_1^r y_1^s \cdots x_m^r \tilde{y}) = \underbrace{0 \cdots 0}_{m}$$

(3.22)

showing that obviously z_i' and z_j' are not equivalent. Since any pairs z_i', z_j', $i \neq j$, of the states $z_1', \ldots, z_m'$ are not equivalent, it follows that $\boldsymbol{B}$ has at least n non-equivalent states. In error detection by duplication and comparison, the state number n is actually reached. Moreover, the dependence of the automaton to be monitored on the components of its, generally multidimen-sional, input variables is transferred to the error detection automaton.

We prove the following proposition.
Let $A = (X = U_1 \times U_2 \times \cdots \times U_k, Y = V_1 \times V_2 \times \cdots \times V_l, z, z_0, f, g)$ be an automaton connected from z_0, with k-dimensional input and l-dimensional output, which actually depends on all of its input components $(u_1, \ldots, u_k)$. Then the error-detecting automaton defined by Eq. (3.12) actually depends on all $(k + l)$ components $(u_1, \ldots, u_k, v_1, \ldots, v_l)$ of its input.

PROOF The actual dependence of $\boldsymbol{B}$ on the components $v_1, \ldots, v_l$ results immediately from the definition (3.12) of $\boldsymbol{B}$, so that we only have to show the actual dependence of $\boldsymbol{B}$ on $u_1, \ldots, u_k$. Since A actually depends on all components of its input, for each i, $1 \leqslant i \leqslant k$, there exists a bit pattern $u_1^0 \cdots u_k^0$ and a $u_i'^0$, $u_i^0 \neq u_i'^0$, such that

$$y_i = g(z_i, (u_1^0, \ldots, u_i^0, \ldots, u_k^0)) \neq g(z_i, (u_1^0, \ldots, u_i'^0, \ldots, u_k^0))$$

$$= y_i', \, y_i = (v_1^i, \ldots, v_l^i), \, y_i' = (v_1'^i, \ldots, v_l'^i)$$

Since A is connected from z_0, there exists an input word $x_1^i, x_2^i \cdots x_m^i$ transfering z_0 into z_i:

$$z_i = f(z_0, x_1^i x_2^i \cdots x_m^i)$$

Denoting $y_1^i y_2^i \cdots y_m^i = g^*(z_0, x_1^i \cdots x_m^i)$, we obtain

$$0 = g_B(z_{0B}, x_1^i y_1^i \cdots x_m^i y_m^i (u_1^0, \ldots, u_i^0, \ldots, u_k^0)(v_1^i, \ldots, v_l^i))$$

$$\neq g_B(z_{0B}, x_1^i y_1^i \cdots x_m^i y_m^i (u_1^0, \ldots, u_i'^0, \ldots, u_k^0)(v_1^i, \ldots, v_l^i))$$

$$= 1$$

which shows that for the state $z_i' = f_B(z_{0B}, x_1^i y_1^i \cdots x_m^i y_m^i)$ in fact g_B actually depends on the ith component of its input vector. The number of states of a circuit and the kind of dependence of the circuit on its input variables describe only a relatively rough approximation to the hardware cost or the complexity of the error detection circuit.

In the special case where $Y = \{0, 1\}$ is binary and the error detection circuit detects every behaviour difference of the circuit to be monitored from that required, it is possible to prove a much more far-reaching proposition about the complexity of the error detection circuit in a simple way. Instead of Eq. (3.12) one has, for $x_1, x_2, \ldots, x_m \in X$, $m > 0$,

$$g_B(z_{0B}, x_1 y_1 \cdots x_m y_m) = \begin{cases} 0 & \text{for } y_m = g(z_0, x_1 \cdots x_m) \\ 1 & \text{for } y_m \neq g(z_0, x_1 \cdots x_m) \end{cases} \qquad (3.12')$$

The error detection circuit B_s according to Eq. (3.12'), in contrast to an error detection circuit according to Eq. (3.12), detects an error of A_s even if it has already indicated an error at an earlier time.

Furthermore, let $K(C_s)$ be a measure of what is required to implement the automaton C with the following properties:

1. $0 < K < \infty$.
2. If C' is a subautomaton of C, then $K(C_s) > K(C'_s)$. Examples of $K(C_s)$ are the number of gates used to implement C, the price of C_s and the computing time required to perform the automated design, etc.

Then the following proposition is true.

Let A_s be an implementation of A that is optimum with respect to K and let B_s be an error detection circuit of A for which (3.12') holds. Then

$$K(B_s) > K(A_s) \qquad (3.23)$$

PROOF Since $Y = \{0, 1\}$, it follows from Eq. (3.12') for $m > 0$ that

$$g(z_{0B}, x_1 y_1 \cdots x_{m-1} y_{m-1} x_m 0) = \begin{cases} 0 & \text{for } 0 = g(z_0, x_1 \cdots x_m) \\ 1 & \text{for } 1 = g(z_0, x_1 \cdots x_m) \end{cases}$$

and hence that

$$g_B(z_0, x_1 0 x_2 0 \cdots x_{m-1} 0 x_m 0) = g(z_0, x_1 \cdots x_m) \qquad (3.24)$$

Consequently, A is initially equivalent to the subautomaton B' of B which results from restricting the input set $X \times \{0, 1\}$ of B to $X \times \{0\}$.

Now suppose that

$$K(B_s) < K(A_s) \qquad (3.25)$$

Since B' is a subautomaton of B, one has

$$K(B'_s) \leqslant K(B_s) < K(A_s)$$

Since, on the other hand, B' is initially equivalent to A, it follows that B'_s is an implementation of A with a K smaller than $K(A_s)$. However, by assuming that A_s is an implementation of A, which is optimum with respect to K, assumption (3.25) actually leads to a contradiction. Consequently, Eq. (3.23) is true.

For the case where A exhibits only a single state, the theorem just proven is a proposition for combinational circuits, which shall now be formulated to conclude this section.

Let $f: X \to \{0, 1\}$ be a combinational function, let f' be the restriction of f to a subset $X' \subseteq X$ and let K be a measure of the implementation cost, with

1. $0 < K < \infty$,
2. $K(f_s) > K(f'_s)$,

then the following is true. If f_s is an implementation of f which is optimum with respect to K, and if ϕ_s is an error detection circuit for f_s with

$$\phi(x, y) = \begin{cases} 0 & \text{for } y = f(x) \\ 1 & \text{for } y \neq f(x) \end{cases}$$

then

$$K(\phi_s) \geqslant K(f_s)$$

Investigations on different measures of expenditure for combinational circuits are presented, for example, in Nigmatullin (1983) and Oberst (1975).

3.9 SUMMARY

In this chapter we have described how sequential error detection circuits can be systematically designed. Sequential circuits are modelled by abstract automata. Basic notions of automata theory were introduced at the beginning of the chapter. Equivalence and compatibility of states allow optimum implementation of automata, and were explained in detail. States of completely defined automata with the same input/output behaviour are called equivalent. Automata that do not have any pairs of equivalent states are called reduced or state minimized. Methods for the state reduction of a given automaton, i.e. the replacement of its states by corresponding equivalence classes of states, are usually implemented on a computer. In technical applications automata to be implemented are often only partially defined. For equivalent states of a completely defined automaton there are corresponding compatible states of partially defined automata.

In the same way as the functional error model of a combinational circuit consists of a set of error functions, the functional error model of a sequential circuit consists of a set of error automata. To every technical fault of the sequential circuit a corresponding error automaton is assigned.

The design of error detection circuits was described at first for automata with observable states. In this case the state behaviour and the output function of the automaton can be separately monitored. In this chapter we have only been concerned with monitoring state behaviour. As long as no erroneous state transition of the monitored automaton occurs the error detection automaton outputs 0 and the states of both the error detection automaton and the monitored automaton are identical. If an erroneous state transition of the monitored automaton takes place which is a possible state transition of one of the error automata of the functional error model, the error detection automaton outputs 1 and its state transition remains undetermined. The state graph of the error detection automaton can be determined by a step-by-step modification of the state graph of the monitored automaton. At every step of this modification one of the error automata of the error model is to be taken into consideration.

After these design steps the partially determined error detection automaton that results possesses exactly as many states as the monitored automaton. The don't-care conditions can now be utilized for the optimization of this automaton into the optimal error detection automaton.

The systematic design of a sequential error detection circuit with observable states can be performed in the following steps:

1. Determine the functional error model based on the component failures to be expected.
2. Determine the partially defined error detection automaton according to Eqs (3.1) and (3.2).
3. Optimize the error detection automaton by existing CAD methods.
4. Implement the optimal error detection automaton.

We have shown that such well-known heuristic methods as duplication and comparison and the application of codes are special cases of the proposed systematic method described. Subsequently we have shown how a coding function of the states of the monitored automaton can be determined in such a way that all errors of a given functional error model can be detected. These heuristic methods were applied to a variety of different, simple examples.

In the general case of non-observable states, the monitored automaton is again modified, step by step, into the corresponding error detection automaton. The first step of modification guarantees that as long as no error occurs, either in the state transition or in the output of the monitored automaton, the error detection automaton outputs 0 and the states of both the error detection automaton and the monitored automaton are identical.

For every automaton of the error model the difference in the visible behaviour of the monitored automaton and the considered error automaton of the functional error model was described by a corresponding error detection tree. All the error detection trees were then processed one after the other again to modify, step by step, the monitored automaton into the error detection automaton. The error detection automaton is again only partially defined.

The error detection automaton detects when the monitored circuit exhibits an incorrect output for the first time, which is a possible output of one of the error automata of the error model. For all the other incorrect outputs, which are not outputs of any error automaton of the error model, the error detection automaton remains undetermined. Again these don't-care conditions are to be utilized to optimize the error detection automaton. The implementation of this optimal error detection automaton is the desired error detection circuit. Due to the step-by-step modification, the partially determined error detection automaton possesses no more states than the monitored automaton in any given design step. Therefore the design of the error detection automaton is of the same order of complexity as the design of the monitored automaton, and a computer aided design of the error detection automaton is possible if the monitored automaton was also designed using CAD tools.

The systematic design of a sequential error detection circuit with non-observable states can be performed in the following steps:

1. Determine the functional error model based on the component failures to be expected.
2. Determine for every error automaton of the functional error model the corresponding error detection tree.
3. Modify the monitored automaton into the error detection automaton in such a way that as long as no error occurs, the states of both the automata are identical and the error detection automaton outputs 0.
4. Process all the error detection trees as described in this chapter.
5. Optimize the resulting partially determined error detection automaton by existing CAD methods.
6. Implement the optimal error detection automaton.

Finally, it was shown how the necessary hardware for error detection can be considerably reduced if some error latency is allowed, or whether the error model is restricted to the most probable errors. At the end of this chapter some limits to the expenditure for error detection were given.

FOUR

DESIGN ALGORITHMS FOR ERROR DETECTION CIRCUITS

In this chapter we will explain how to design error detection circuits using computer aided procedures. To begin with, we show how the method described in Chapter 3 for the determination of an error detection automaton can be translated into an algorithm that can practicably be implemented on a computer in order to design circuits of practical orders of magnitude. The calculation of the error-detecting function for combinational circuits will be presented as a special case.

For a given error detection automaton, the computer aided design of an optimum error detection circuit is a normal—and thus widely performed—design task. Therefore, we discuss below some of the more common known computer aided design systems, pointing out some peculiarities in the design of error detection circuitry.

Computer aided design makes it possible to design error detection circuits for actual digital circuitry. With the use of modern design tools, complex digital circuits are subdivided into subcircuits of a size that can still be mastered by individual designers. In the case of the logical connection of data vectors these subcircuits include only a few of the bits. Also, previous experience has shown that only in rare cases do problems occur in the design of different control circuits where the number of binary inputs and outputs is greater than 20, without any possibility of a reasonable decomposition, and thus simplification.

For such subcircuits, whose design is still to be mastered, it is also possible to design error detection circuits by computer aided methods. The error detection circuit for the overall circuitry has then to be combined from the subcircuits.

4.1 PRACTICABLE ALGORITHM

We shall now describe an algorithm which, for a given automaton A with the error model $F(A) = \{A_0 = A, A_1, \ldots, A_n\}$ determines an error detection automaton B by the method presented in Sec. 3.1. We assume that at an arbitrary time the automaton A is disturbed to change into one of the automata A_i of the error model. In the special case where A as well as all of the automata $A_1, \ldots, A_n$ of the error model have only a single state each, this algorithm yields an error detection function according to Sec. 2.1 for a combinational function f.

Let the inputs, outputs and states of all automata be binary coded and let

$$X \subseteq \{0, 1\}^{l_x}, \ Y \subseteq \{0, 1\}^{l_y}, \ Z \subseteq \{0, 1\}^{l_z}, \ Z_i \subseteq \{0, 1\}^{l_z}, \quad i = 1, \ldots, n$$

The program flow-chart, which implements the following algorithm, is shown in Fig. 4.1.

The automata table obtained for the error detection automaton B and the automata table of one of the automata A_i of the error model $F(A)$ are stored in two files named TAB and BLOCK. The length of a row in TAB and BLOCK, respectively, is $l_x + l_y + 2l_z + 1$ and $l_x + l_y + 2l_z$. Data of the form x, y, z, z', y_F, with $x \in X$, $y \in Y$, $z \in Z$, $z' = f_B(z, xy)$, $y_F = g_B(z, xy)$, are entered into a row of TAB, and data of the form x, y, z, z', with $x \in X$, $y = g_i(z, x)$, $z \in Z_i, z' = f_i(z, x)$, are entered into a row of BLOCK. To record the execution status of the algorithm, the two fields WL (waiting list) and MB (memory field) are used. Both of them have a row length of $2l_z$. State pairs $(z, \tilde{z})$, $z \in Z$, $\tilde{z} \in Z_i$, are written into the fields of WL and MB. The algorithm is so designed that at any time only the minimum necessary storage is used.

After reading in the parameters m, l_x, l_y, l_z, the quantities

$$x, g(z, x), z, f(z, x), 0 \quad \text{for } x \in X \text{ and } z \in Z$$

are written into the first rows of TAB. The functions f and g are, as already pointed out, the state transition function and the output function, respectively, of the standard automaton $A = A_0$. Thus A_0 has been read into TAB. For the error-free behaviour of the circuit A_s to be implemented, the behaviour of the error detection automaton B is already completely determined. It should be noted that the automata of the error model may only cause rows to be added to TAB in which $y_F = 1$ or $Y_F = -$ (don't care). To take account of the automaton A_i of the error model, the quantities

$$x, g_i(z, x), z, f_i(z, x) \quad \text{for } x \in X \text{ and } z \in Z_i$$

are entered into the BLOCK file; this is abbreviated to A_i and is entered into BLOCK.

Since we assume that the error 'A disturbed to change into A_i' may occur at any time, and hence in any state $z \in Z$ of the automaton A, we have

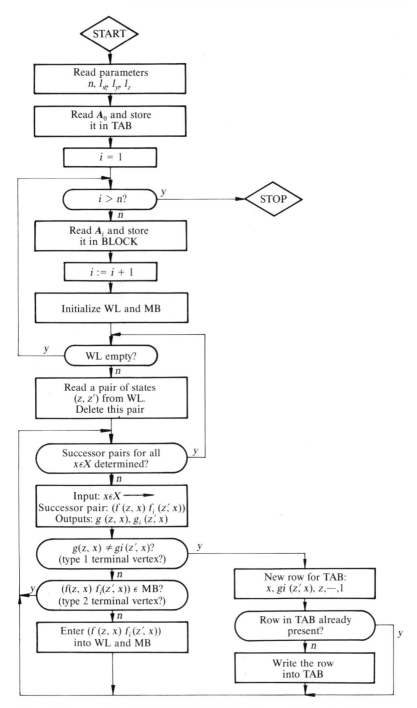

Figure 4.1 Program flow-chart for the CAD design of error detection circuits.

to investigate error detection trees B_i^z with the root (z, z) for all $z \in Z$ (which can be reached from z_0). All state pairs (z, z) with $z \in Z$ are entered into the waiting list WL and the memory field MB, after A_i has been read into BLOCK. We abbreviate this by saying that WL and MB are initialized. For a state pair (z, z'') taken from the waiting list, the quantities $g(z, x)$, $g_i(z'', x)$ and $f(z, x)$, $f_i(z'', x)$ are now determined, one after the other, for all $x \in X$. The pair (z, z'') is deleted from the waiting list WL. If $g(z, x) \neq g_i(z'', x)$, then we have a type 1 terminal vertex, and a row containing the data

$$x, \ g_i(z'', x), \ z, \ \text{—(don't care)}, \ 1$$

is added to TAB, provided it is not yet contained in TAB. In the automata graph of B, this step corresponds to adding an edge marked $(x, g_i(z'', x))$, 1, which leads from the state z and whose end point remains free.

If $g(z, x) = g_i(z'', x)$, then it must be checked whether $(f(z, x), f_i(z'', x))$ is a type 2 terminal vertex. This can be done by checking whether $(f(z, x), f_i(z'', x))$ is stored in the memory field MB. If there is no type 2 terminal vertex, then $(f(z, x), f_i(z'', x))$ is entered into WL and MB. If the node is a type 2 terminal vertex, then no entries are made into WL or MB.

When all entries have been deleted from the waiting list WL, then the automaton A_i of the error model $F(A)$ has been fully taken into account. This sequence is repeated for all automata A_i of the error model, one after the other.

After completion of the program, TAB contains all the rows of the automata table of B for which $y_F = 0$ or $y_F = 1$. For all rows not listed in TAB one has $y_F = $ —(don't care) and $z' = $ —(don't care). When initializing the memory field MB with the pairs (z, z), $z \in Z$, we shorten the algorithm by immediately entering into the memory field MB all those pairs of nodes that occur as roots of an error detection tree and are written into the waiting list WL. They are then treated as type 2 terminal vertices if they occur as successor states of another pair of states. Since they are stored in the waiting list WL as a root of an error detection tree, the continuation from these nodes will be investigated in any case, although this may be later on. The algorithm described above can be used to calculate the error-detecting function for combinational circuits if the combinational functions are regarded as single-state automata. The standard function $f = f_0$ and the functions of the error model $F(f) = \{f_1, \ldots, f_n\}$ are each permanently assigned the 'state zero'. The waiting list WL and the memory field MB are both initialized with $(0, 0)$. The columns for z and z' in the files TAB and BLOCK can be saved, because they would always contain zeros in the combinational case.

Then data of the form

$$x, \ y, \ y_F \quad \text{with} \quad x \in X, \ y \in Y, \ y_F = \phi(x, y)$$

are written into a row of the TAB file, and data of the form

$$x, y \quad \text{with} \quad x \in X \quad \text{and} \quad y \in Y$$

are entered into a row of the BLOCK file. For $x \in X$, the data

$$x, f(x), 0$$

are written into the first rows of TAB.

To take account of the error function f_i of the error model $F(f)$ for $x \in X$ the data

$$x, f_i(x)$$

are written into the BLOCK file. Then for all $x \in X$ the condition $f(x) \neq f_i(x)$ is checked. If $f(x) \neq f_i(x)$ is satisfied, then in TAB a row with the data

$$x, f_i(x), 1$$

is added, provided such a row is not already present in TAB.

For $f(x) = f_i(x)$ the result of the test for a type 2 terminal vertex is always positive. After completion of the program, TAB contains all the rows of the error-detecting function ϕ for which either $\phi(x, y) = 0$ or $\phi(x, y) = 1$. For all values not listed in TAB one has $\phi(x, y) = -$(don't care).

For the sequential case, let us now illustrate the algorithm by a simple example, a Gray-code counter

$$A = (\{0, 1\}, \{00, 01, 10, 11\}, \{00, 01, 10, 11\}, z_0 = 00, f, g)$$

with $f = g$ and with the functional error model $F(A) = \{A_0 = A, A_1, \ldots, A_{10}\}$, $A_i = (\{0, 1\}, \{00, 01, 10, 11\}, \{00, 01, 10, 11\}, z_{0i} = 00, f_i, g_i), i = 1, \ldots, 10$. The state transition functions $f, f_1, \ldots, f_{10}$ are described in Table 4.1.

For the automaton A and the automata $A_i \in F(A)$ of the error model, $g(z, x) = f(z, x)$ and $g_i(z, x) = f_i(z, x)$, $i = 1, \ldots, 10$, respectively, is satisfied for all $x \in X = \{0, 1\}$ and all $z \in Z = \{00, 01, 10, 11\}$, so that only the functions f and f_i are described in Table 4.1.

Table 4.1

x	z	f	f_1	f_2	f_3	f_4	f_5	f_6	f_7	f_8	f_9	f_{10}
0	00	00	00	00	00	00	00	00	00	00	00	00
0	01	01	00	01	01	01	01	00	01	00	01	00
0	10	10	00	10	00	10	10	10	00	10	00	10
0	11	11	00	11	01	11	11	10	01	11	01	10
1	00	01	01	00	01	01	00	01	01	00	01	00
1	01	11	11	10	11	01	10	11	01	10	01	10
1	10	00	00	00	00	00	00	00	00	00	00	00
1	11	10	10	10	10	00	10	10	00	10	00	10

Table 4.2

No.	x	y	z	z'	y_F
1	0	00	00	00	0
2	0	01	01	01	0
3	0	10	10	10	0
4	0	11	11	11	0
5	1	01	00	01	0
6	1	11	01	11	0
7	1	00	10	00	0
8	1	10	11	10	0
9	0	00	11	—	1
10	0	00	10	—	1
11	0	00	01	—	1
12	0	01	11	—	1
13	0	10	11	—	1
14	1	00	11	—	1
15	1	01	01	—	1
16	1	10	01	—	1
17	1	00	00	—	1

One has $l_x = 1$, $l_y = 2$, $l_z = 2$ and $n = 10$. Thus the rows of TAB are 8 bits long and the rows of BLOCK are 7 bits long. The automata table of $A = A_0$ is 8 rows long. When this table is read into TAB, the first 8 rows of this file are occupied. For these rows one has $y_F = 0$ (see Table 4.2). Now the automata table of the automaton A_1 is read into the BLOCK file, whose bit contents is shown in Table 4.3.

The waiting list WL and the memory field MB are initialized with (z, z), $z \in Z$, i.e. with $(00, 00)$, $(01, 01)$, $(10, 10)$, $(11, 11)$. Subsequently, a pair of states (z, z''), here for instance $(11, 11)$, is taken from the waiting list WL and deleted in WL. Now for all $x \in \{0, 1\}$ one has to find all pairs of outputs $g(11, x)$, $g_1(11, x)$ and all pairs of successor states $f(11, x)$, $f_1(11, x)$ which

Table 4.3

No.	x	y	z	z'
1	0	00	00	00
2	0	00	01	00
3	0	00	10	00
4	0	00	11	00
5	1	01	00	01
6	1	11	01	11
7	1	00	10	00
8	1	10	11	10

are determined from the first 8 rows of TAB and the actual rows of BLOCK. For $x = 0$ one obtains $(g(11, 0), g_1(11, 0)) = (11, 00)$, $(f(11, 0), f_1(11, 0)) = (11, 0)$.

Since $g(11, 0) \neq g_1(11, 0)$, it follows that $(f(11, 0), f_1(11, 0))$ is a type 1 terminal vertex, so that a row with

$$x = 0, \ y = g_1(11, 0) = 00, \ z = 11, \ z' = —, \ y_F = 1$$

has to be entered into TAB, because such a row is not yet contained in TAB. It is entered into Table 4.2 as the ninth row.

For $x = 1$, from Tables 4.2 and 4.3 (the eighth row of each) we obtain $g(11, 1) = 10$, $g_1(11, 1) = 10$, $f(11, 1) = 10$, $f_1(11, 1) = 10$, so that $(10, 10)$ is not a type 1 terminal vertex. Therefore the test for a type 2 terminal vertex is applied. The pair of states $(10, 10)$ is already contained in MB, and $(10, 10)$ is a type 2 terminal vertex, not to be processed further here. The next pair of states taken from the waiting list WL is $(10, 10)$. The processing of this pair of states yields a type 1 terminal vertex $(10, 00)$, which is taken into account in TAB by row 10 in Table 4.2. The successor pair of the pair of states $(01, 01)$ taken from the waiting list WL is found to be the type 1 terminal vertex $(01, 00)$. It is taken into account by row 11 in Table 4.2. All other successor pairs of $(10, 10)$, $(01, 01)$ and $(00, 00)$ are type 2 terminal vertices, so no other pairs need to be entered into WL. After the pair of states $(00, 00)$ has been processed, the waiting list is empty.

In the next step the automata table of A_2 is read into BLOCK, and the waiting list WL as well as the memory field MB are again initialized with $(00, 00)$, $(01, 01)$, $(10, 10)$ and $(11, 11)$. Processing the automata A_2 to A_{10} gives the rows 12 to 17 in Table 4.2.

Since $l_x = 1$, $l_y = l_z = 2$, TAB has $2^5 = 32$ rows. For the rows 18 to 32, which are not listed in Table 4.2, one has $y_F = —$(don't care) and $z' = —$(don't care). The automata table of the automaton B shown in Table 4.2 is the starting point of the subsequent normal design of a sequential circuit. The don't-care conditions of the transition function (ninth to thirty-second rows) and of the output function (eighteenth to thirty-second rows) have to be utilized for optimization.

4.2 DESIGN OPTIMIZATION AND IMPLEMENTATION

We shall now describe known design program systems for digital circuits that can be used in the design of an optimum implementation B_s of the partially defined error detection automaton B or in an optimum implementation ϕ_s of the partially defined error detection function ϕ. Apart from many individual programs for the solution of special design problems there exist program packages for supporting whole stages of design and extensive CAD systems that are suitable to use in the development of a digital unit from conception to the beginning of production.

The CAD systems are usually designed as open systems of largely autonomous programs. Thus it is always possible to add user-specific extensions. Variants of large program packages used to support the design of digital units are described in Case (1981), Newton *et al.* (1981), Raymond (1981), Mauck (1983), Darringer (1984), Koch and Nett (1984) and Hörbst *et al.* (1986).

The support of the design optimization by CAD systems is in effect based on three different approaches. These are:

1. Use of optimization methods for partially defined Boolean functions and partially defined automata.
2. Optimization of a circuit by great number of local steps adapted on a specific technological basis.
3. Use of preoptimized 'logic macros' such as registers, ALUs, counters, decoders, etc.

At present the last two variants are frequently given priority in CAD systems (cf. Raymond, 1981; Darringer, 1984; Koch and Nett, 1984). One starts from the fact that optimization methods for Boolean functions and for partial automata require a computing time that increases exponentially with problem size; therefore the methods are not suited for processing larger circuits. This statement may be qualified by the use of rapidly converging approximation methods and the decomposition of the circuit into surveyable subcircuits, which is required in any case in the design.

In the design of error detection circuits, the saving that results from minimization of the partially defined error detection function or of the partially defined error detection automaton by utilizing the don't-care conditions is of special interest. Here, we especially refer to CAD systems and individual programs that support such optimizations. If the principles of structuring CAD systems presented in Pilz (1984) are observed, then, if required, optimization algorithms can also be implemented.

The CAMP (computer aided minimization procedure) program described in Biswas (1984) for the optimization of Boolean functions leads to good approximate solutions using only a few iterative steps. It allows problems with a large number of variables (at least 30) to be processed within favourable processing times. The data can be input in the form of tables of values. A special algorithm for determining prime conjunctions quickly is described in Heltzig and Oberst (1973). The problem description is also performed by means of tables of values.

In Anonymous (1983), reference is made to the LOGE program system, which has been in commercial use since 1982. It supports the design of digital circuits in all stages and contains special synthesis programs. The design of optimized error detection circuits should immediately be possible using this CAD system. It should be pointed out that there are some peculiarities that have to be taken into consideration in the physical/technical design of error detection circuits. Depending on how the error detection circuit is to be applied, a permissible time interval is determined, during which the error signal must be generated. This makes a defined response of the system possible in order to monitor an error indication within a specified time. By means of components with a favourable delay and by selecting a suitable circuit structure it is possible to improve the time-based properties of an error detection circuit. From the programming aspect, selection of a certain circuit structure can be supported by suitable bracketing rules in the derivation of formulas. If necessary, the error model must be restricted or delayed error detection will result.

An error detection circuit receives the input and output signals of the circuit to be monitored. It is a consumer in the network of the original circuit. Apart from the permissible maximum load of the source components, it must be understood that as a consumer the error detection circuit affects the switching behaviour of the components of the circuit to be monitored. This effect depends on the technology used. If applicable, isolating amplifiers are required at the interface between the error detection circuit and the circuit to be monitored, as shown in Fig. 4.2.

If for several subcircuits of the overall circuit one error detection circuit has been designed individually, then a global error signal can be produced by logical OR of the outputs of the error detection circuits corresponding to the subcircuits. This increases the signal delay up to the output of an error signal.

A task of ever-increasing importance to circuit design is the design of circuits that are easy to diagnose and easy to test. Possible solutions of this problem range from the simple diagnosis adapter over signal selection pyramids to the LSSD (level sensitive scan design) (Berglund, 1979; Roth, 1980). The LSSD makes it possible in the diagnosis mode to interconnect

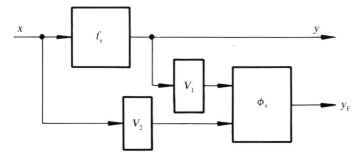

Figure 4.2 Error detection circuit with isolating amplifiers V_1 and V_2.

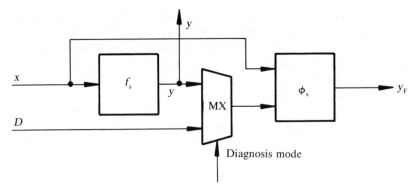

Figure 4.3 Error detection circuit with additional external test input *D*.

all internal flip-flops to shift registers whose contents can then be shifted out sequentially and thus compared with what the overall state of the circuit should be. Here, the error detection circuit has to be included in these measures as part of the overall circuitry. A peculiarity results if the error detection circuit is also to be tested. The error signal 1 appears at the output of the error detection circuit only if erroneous input bit patterns are applied to the error detection circuit. Therefore the presence of a stuck-at-0 error at the output of the error detection circuit can only be tested by means of additional hardware. Thus, for instance, it is possible to provide an additional external input *D*, which, instead of the circuit output *y*, in the diagnostic mode is connected via a multiplexer MX to the input of the error detection

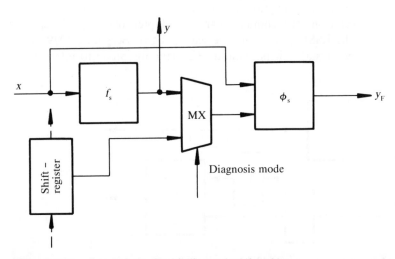

Figure 4.4 Error detection circuit with diagnostic shift register.

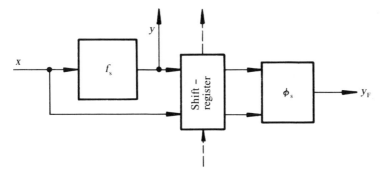

Figure 4.5 Error detection circuit with a special variant of a diagnostic shift register.

circuit ϕ_s (see Fig. 4.3). Here the additional connection D may also utilize data paths that are otherwise used in the normal operation of the circuit.

It is also possible to use diagnostic shift registers, as shown in Figs 4.4 and 4.5. These registers are serially loaded in the preparation phase of the test step, and then apply the data stored in them to corresponding inputs of the error detection circuit. The variant shown in Fig. 4.5 represents a special case. Here the circuit f_s is isolated from the error detection circuit ϕ_s, also in normal operation by a register, which at the same time is included in a diagnostic shifting cascade. In this solution, which is very favourable with respect to overhead, the error signal is generated after a delay. If, in the case of sequential circuits, a synchronizing pulse sequence is not possible or not provided, then both circuits have to be connected to a central reset pulse.

4.3 SUMMARY

In this chapter, we have shown how the methods for the systematic design of sequential and combinational error detection circuits can practically be implemented as an algorithm on a computer. The algorithm was implemented in such a way that at any time only the minimum necessary storage was used. The data organization of the algorithm, in the form of different tables of values, and the data management are described in detail.

The computer aided design of a partially defined automaton is an integral part of the overall design of an optimal error detection circuit. Therefore we have also referred to some well-known CAD systems and pointed out some of the peculiarities of such systems, which are of interest in the design of error detection circuitry.

THE ERROR MODEL

Depending upon the technology, logic gates and memory elements are implemented at a physical level by transistors and diodes. Faulty gates or faulty circuits are due to physical defects or failures or are due to design errors. If a deviation of the behaviour of a faulty circuit from that of the correct circuit is externally visible then an error occurs.

Physical failures are, for example, a shortage to ground of a line, a shortage of a line to the power supply, broken lines, bridging between lines, faults caused by α-radiation or electromagnetic fields (including crosstalk). Faults may be permanent or transient. Transient faults occur only for a specific (short) time. They are hard to detect by testing alone, but they can be detected by error detection circuits during operation.

In this book, faults of a circuit are described by a functional error model. A functional error model $F(A)$ of a circuit A_s, for implementing the automaton A, is a set of automata $\{A = A_0, A_1, \ldots, A_K\}$. The automata $A_1, \ldots, A_K$ of the error model $F(A)$ are those automata that may be implemented by the circuit A_s instead of A when a physical or technical failure that is considered occurs.

If f_s is a combinational circuit used to implement a combinational function f very often (but not in all cases) the error model $F(f) = \{f_0 = f, f_1, \ldots, f_K\}$ is a set of combinational functions $f_1, \ldots, f_K$. The functions $f_1, \ldots, f_K$ are called the error functions of $F(f)$.

A.1 STUCK-AT-0/1 FAULTS

If a line of a circuit is fixed to either 0 (low) or 1 (high) we say that the line is stuck-at-0 or stuck-at-1. Figure A.1 shows an AND gate whose input and

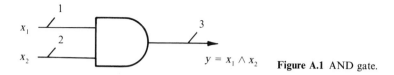

Figure A.1 AND gate.

output lines are numbered from 1 to 3. If the line 1 is fixed to 1 the faulty AND element implements the error function $f_1(x_1, x_2) = 1 \wedge x_2 = x_2$. In the case where the line 2 is stuck-at-1 the faulty AND element implements the error function $f_2(x_1, x_2) = x_1 \wedge 1 = x_1$. The error function $f_3(x_1, x_2) = 1$ is caused by a stuck-at-1 fault of the line 3 of the AND gate.

The functional error model

$$F_1(x_1, x_2) = \{f_0(x_1, x_2) = x_1 \wedge x_2, f_1(x_1, x_2) = x_2, f_2(x_1, x_2) = x_1, f_3(x_1, x_2) = 1\}$$

corresponds to the technical faults stuck-at-1 of a single line. The technical faults result from physical failures mentioned above. If one of the lines 1, 2 or 3 is stuck-at-0 the faulty AND gate implements the error function $f_4(x_1, x_2) = 0 \wedge x_2 = x_1 \wedge 0 = 0$. If we suppose that only single stuck-at-0 faults occur, the error model of the AND gate is

$$F_0(x_1 \wedge x_2) = \{f_0(x_1, x_2) = x_1 \wedge x_2, f_4(x_1, x_2) = 0\}$$

If both stuck-at-1 and stuck-at-0 faults are to be considered, the corresponding functional error model is

$$F_{0,1}(x_1 \wedge x_2) = \{x_1 \wedge x_2, x_2, x_1, 1, 0\}$$

A.2 BRIDGING FAULTS

If, due to a physical defect, two or more wires of a circuit are wrongly connected together, a bridging fault occurs. Depending on which technology is used, a 'wired OR' or a 'wired AND' of the connected lines may result. Bridging faults are easy to model using a functional error model if feedback is not generated due to the bridging.

Let us consider some examples of bridging faults and suppose that a 'wired AND' is generated by bridging. The combinational circuit f_s of Fig. A.2(a) implements the function $f(x_1, x_2, x_3) = (x_1 \vee x_2)x_3$. If bridging between input line 1 and input line 2 occurs, a 'wired AND' between line 1 and line 2 results and the faulty circuit of Fig. A.2(a) is functionally replaced by the circuit of Fig. A.2(b) which implements the error function $x_1 \wedge x_2 \wedge x_3$. Thus the functional error model $F_{1,2}(f)$ due to bridging of the lines 1 and 2 is given by

$$F_{1,2}(f) = \{(x_1 \vee x_2)x_3, x_1 \wedge x_2 \wedge x_3\}$$

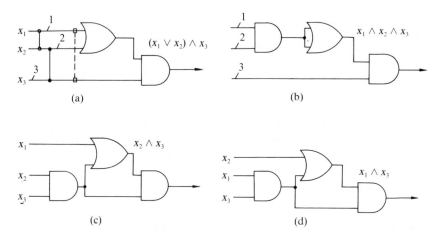

Figure A.2 Combinational circuit and its bridging faults.

In the case of bridging between the lines 2 and 3 or 1 and 3, the faulty circuit f_s is functionally replaced by the circuits of Fig. A.2(c) and (d) implementing the functions $x_2 \wedge x_3$ or $x_1 \wedge x_3$, respectively. Thus the functional error model $F_{\text{brid}}(f)$ corresponding to one bridging fault between two input lines is determined by

$$F_{\text{brid}}(f) = \{(x_1 \vee x_2)x_3, x_1 \wedge x_2 \wedge x_3, x_2 \wedge x_3, x_1 \wedge x_3\}$$

Due to the bridging of input and output lines of a combinational circuit feedback is generated, making it much more complicated to model this type of fault (cf., for example, Lala, 1985).

Let us suppose now that the bridging of lines results in a 'wired OR'. Figure A.3 shows a combinational circuit f_s for implementing the XOR $y = x_1 \oplus x_2$. Suppose that the bridging occurs between the output line and input line 1. Then the circuit of Fig. A.3 is functionally replaced by the circuit of Fig. A.4.

Since we have $0 \oplus 1 = 1$ and $1 \oplus 1 = 0$, for $x_1 = 0$ and $x_2 = 1$ the output y oscillates between 1 and 0. This cannot be modelled by a functional error model consisting of a set of purely deterministic automata. Figure A.5 shows a combinational circuit f_s (gate) for implementing the conjunction $y = x_1 \wedge x_2$.

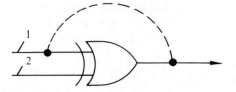

Figure A.3 Bridging between input and output of an XOR gate.

Again, suppose that a bridging fault occurs between the output and input line 1. The circuit of Fig. A.5 is functionally replaced by the circuit of Fig. A.6. The circuit of Fig. A.6 can functionally be described by an automaton A_1 defined by Table A.1. In the case $x_1 = 0$, $x_2(t) = 1$ the automaton A_1 outputs $y(t) = y(t - 1)$; in all other cases $y(t) = x_1(t) \land x_2(t)$. This bridging fault can therefore be described by the functional error model

$$F_{\text{brid}}(x_1 \land x_2) = \{x_1 \land x_2, A_1\}$$

A somewhat more detailed description of bridging faults is contained in Lala (1985).

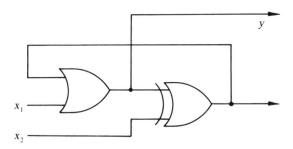

Figure A.4 Oscillating behaviour resulting from bridging.

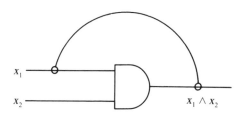

Figure A.5 Bridging between input and output of an AND gate.

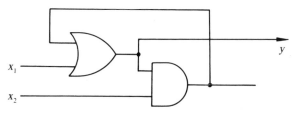

Figure A.6 Sequential behaviour resulting from bridging.

Table A.1

$x_1(t)$	$x_2(t)$	$y(t-1)$	$y(t)$
0	0	0	0
0	0	1	0
0	1	0	0
0	1	1	1
1	0	0	0
1	0	1	0
1	1	0	1
1	1	1	1

A.3 STUCK-OPEN FAULTS

Stuck-open faults are physical faults that may occur in CMOS technology. They change a combinational circuit f_s for implementing a combinational function f into an erroneous sequential circuit, because the output of the gate may be floating for some input set (and therefore may retain its previous state for an almost arbitrary time). Functionally these faults can be modelled by abstract automata.

Figure A.7 shows a NOR gate for implementing the function

$$f(x_1, x_2) = \overline{x_1 \vee x_2} = \text{NOR}(x_1, x_2)$$

According to Lala (1985) the functional description of three single stuck-open faults for the considered CMOS NOR gate is given in Table A.2.

From Table A.2 we have

$$y_1(t) = \text{NOR}(x_1(t), x_2(t)) \vee \bar{x}_1(t) \wedge x_2(t) \wedge y(t-1)$$
$$= g_1(z(t), x_1(t), x_2(t))$$
$$y_2(t) = \text{NOR}(x_1(t), x_2(t)) \vee x_1(t) \wedge \bar{x}_2(t) \wedge y(t-1)$$
$$= g_2(z(t), x_1(t), x_2(t))$$
$$y_3(t) = \text{NOR}(x_1(t), x_2(t)) \oplus \bar{x}_1(t) \wedge \bar{x}_2(t) \wedge \bar{y}(t-1)$$
$$= \bar{x}_1(t) \wedge \bar{x}_2(t) \wedge y(t-1)$$
$$= g_3(z(t), x_1(t), x_2(t))$$

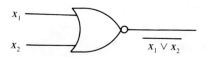

x_1

x_2

$\overline{x_1 \vee x_2}$

Figure A.7 NOR gate.

Table A.2

$x_2(t)$	$x_1(t)$	$y(t-1)$	$\overline{x_1(t) \vee x_2}$	y_1	y_2	y_3
0	0	0	1	1	1	0
0	0	1	1	1	1	1
0	1	0	0	0	0	0
0	1	1	0	0	1	0
1	0	1	0	0	0	0
1	0	1	0	1	0	0
1	1	0	0	0	0	0
1	1	1	0	0	0	0

with

$$z(t) = y(t-1)$$

The functional error model of the considered CMOS NOR gate is

$$F(f_s) = \{\text{NOR}(x_1, x_2), A_1, A_2, A_3\}$$

with

$$A_i = (\{0, 1\}^2, \{0, 1\}, \{0, 1\}, f_i, g_i\})$$

and

$$z(t + 1) = f_i(z(t), x_1(t), x_2(t))$$

$$f_i(z, x_1, x_2) = g_i(z, x_1, x_2), \qquad i = 1, 2, 3$$

It is of interest to mention here that even an exhaustive test may not detect every stuck-open fault. To demonstrate this, let us consider the case where f_s implements the automaton A_1 instead of f. If the exhaustive test sequence for the CMOS NOR gate is 00, 01, 10, 11, the test responses are 1, 0, 0, 0 and no error is indicated. (It is left to the reader to determine a test sequence that detects every error A_1, A_2, A_3 of the functional error model of the CMOS NOR gate.)

Due to the long and relatively complicated test sequences for combinational CMOS circuits, which in the case of an error may implement sequential circuits, error detection circuits have many benefits for such circuits. (To some extent, sequential behaviour for stuck-open faults may be avoided by special design techniques.)

A.4 INDEPENDENT OUTPUTS

Let us suppose that two outputs of a circuit under consideration are implemented without any common gates. Then we can say that these two outputs are independent. If we assume that at most a single gate is faulty then, at most, one of the two independent outputs may be erroneous.

An error in which both of the independent outputs are simultaneously erroneous is not an error of the error model considered. To conclude this we do not need to know the internal structure of the considered circuit except that the two outputs are independent. This fact can be directly used to determine don't-care conditions for the error-detecting function of a combinational circuit which is to be monitored. Figure A.8 shows an implementation of a 1-bit adder.

In Fig. A.8 it is shown that the sum S and the carry c_+ are independent (A and B are binary operands, c_- is the carry-in). For the correct sum S_0 and the correct carry-out c_+ we have

$$S_0 = A \oplus B \oplus c_-$$

$$c_{+0} = (A \wedge B) \vee (A \wedge c_-) \vee (B \wedge c_-)$$

The error detection function ϕ may be determined by

$$\phi(A, B, c_-, s, c_+) = \begin{cases} 0 & \text{for } S = S_0 \text{ and } c_+ = c_{+0} \\ 1 & \text{for } S \neq S_0 \text{ and } c_+ = c_{+0} \text{ or } S = S_0 \text{ and } c_+ \neq c_{+0} \\ - & \text{for } S \neq S_0 \text{ and } c_+ \neq c_{+0} \end{cases}$$

$$(A.1)$$

If we had a more detailed knowledge about the internal structure of the circuit and about the possible technical faults, more don't-care conditions in Eq. (A.1) could occur. However, the don't-care conditions in the last line of Eq. (A.1) are determined by the fact that the sum and the carry-out output of the considered adder are independent. In these cases a detailed description of a possible large set of error functions may be avoided.

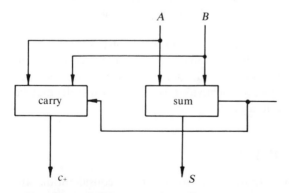

Figure A.8 1-bit adder. The sum and the carry-out are independently implemented.

A.5 SIMPLE FUNCTIONAL ERROR MODEL

For the example of a Gray-code counter we discuss here how a given set of technical faults can be described by a simple functional error model. Figure A.9 shows an implementation of a Gray-code counter A with four states. The gates and the memory elements of A are numbered from 1 to 11. The input line is marked by 12. The state transition function f of the Gray-code counter $A = (\{0, 1\}, \{00, 01, 10, 11\}, 00, f)$ is represented in Table A.3. Thus we have

$$z'_1 = z_1 \wedge \bar{x} \vee \bar{z}_2 \wedge x$$
$$z'_2 = z_1 \wedge x \vee z_2 \wedge \bar{x}$$

(A.2)

We suppose that the input line x or one of the output lines of one of the gates or memory elements may be stuck-at-$0/1$. If such a technical fault occurs we need to replace the element i considered by the corresponding

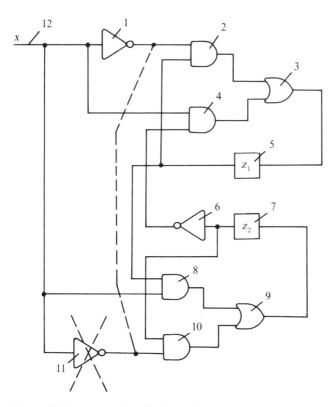

Figure A.9 Implementation of a Gray-code counter.

Table A.3

z_2	z_1	x	$f(z_2, z_1, x)$
0	0	0	00
0	1	0	01
1	1	0	11
1	0	0	10
0	0	1	01
0	1	1	11
1	1	1	10
1	0	1	00

faulty element and, instead of A, one of the erroneous automata

$$A_{i,j} = (\{0, 1\}, \{00, 01, 10, 11\}, 00, f_i, g_j), \qquad i \in \{1, \dots, 12\}, j \in \{0, 1\}$$

of the functional error model $F(A)$ will be implemented by the faulty circuit of Fig. A.9. If the output line of gate 1 is stuck-at-0, instead of Eq. (A.1) we have

$$z'_1 = \bar{z}_2 \wedge x$$
$$z'_2 = z_1 \wedge x \vee z_2 \wedge \bar{x} \qquad (A.3)$$

which describes the automaton $A_{1,0}$ of the error model $F(A)$. In the case where the output line of gate 1 is stuck at 1, the corresponding automaton $A_{1,1}$ of the error model $F(A)$ is given by

$$z'_1 = z_1 \vee \bar{z}_2 \wedge x$$
$$z'_2 = z_1 \wedge x \vee z_2 \wedge \bar{x} \qquad (A.4)$$

The second lines of Eqs (A.2), (A.3) and (A.4) describing the second component of the state transition are identical. Differences in the state transition between A and $A_{1,0}$ and A and $A_{1,1}$ only concern the first component z_1 of the state vector (z_2, z_1). Therefore only single-bit errors of the state transition may be caused by a stuck-at-0/1 fault of the output of the gate 1. It is easy to see that only single-bit errors of the state transition may be caused by stuck-at-0/1 faults of gates 2, 3, 4, 6, 8, 9, 10, 11.

Now suppose that the output of the memory element 5 is stuck-at-0. Then instead of eq. (A.2) we have

$$z'_1 = \bar{z}_2 \wedge x$$
$$z'_2 = z_2 \wedge \bar{x} \qquad (A.5)$$

The state diagrams of the automata $A_{5,0}$ and A are shown in Fig. A.10. Comparing the state diagrams of $A_{5,0}$ and A we see that even in this case only single-bit errors of the state transition occur.

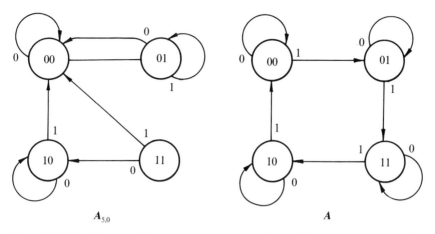

Figure A.10 State diagram of the erroneous automaton $A_{5,0}$ and the correct automaton A.

The stuck-at-0/1 faults of the input line x modify the automaton A into $A_{12,0}$ and $A_{12,1}$, respectively, with

$$z_1' = z_1$$
$$z_2' = z_2 \tag{A.6}$$

for $A_{12,0}$ and

$$z_1' = \bar{z}_2$$
$$z_2' = z_1 \tag{A.7}$$

for $A_{12,1}$. The corresponding state diagrams of $A_{12,0}$ and $A_{12,1}$ are shown in Fig. A.11. Comparing $A_{12,0}$ and $A_{12,1}$ with A, it can be seen that again only single-bit errors of the state transition occur.

If we replace, in a similar way, all the elements i, $i = 1, \ldots, 12$, step by step by corresponding faulty elements only single-bit errors of the state transition of the erroneous automata $A_{i,0}$ and $A_{i,1}$ occur. Thus we are able to model these errors by an error model $F'(A) = \{A_0, A_1, \ldots, A_{16}\}$ consisting of A and 16 erroneous automata A_i:

$$A_i = (\{0, 1\}, \{00, 01, 10, 11\}, 00, f_i), \qquad i = 1, \ldots, 16$$

which differ from A in exactly one state transition. This erroneous state transition differs from the corresponding state transition of the correct automaton A in exactly one bit. Thus for the automaton A_1 we have

$$f_1(z, x) = \begin{cases} 01 & \text{for } z = 00 \text{ and } x = 0 \\ f(z, x) & \text{otherwise} \end{cases}$$

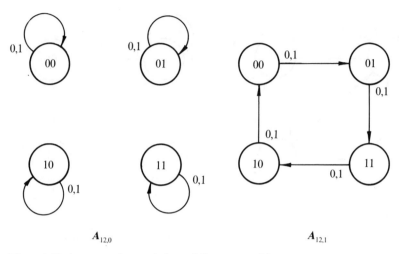

$$A_{12,0} \qquad\qquad A_{12,1}$$

Figure A.11 Automata $A_{12,0}$ and $A_{12,1}$ of the error model.

Besides the state transition $f_1(00, 0) = 01$, which differs from $f(00, 0) = 00$ in exactly one bit, A_1 and A are identical. In a shortened form A_1 can be described by $f_1(00, 0) = 01$. The automaton A_2 is defined by

$$f_2(z, x) = \begin{cases} 10 & \text{for } z = 00 \text{ and } x = 0 \\ f(z, x) & \text{otherwise} \end{cases}$$

and its shortened form is $f_2(00, 0) = 10$. In the shortened form the automata A_i, $i = 1, \ldots, 16$, which differ from A in one bit of one state transition of the error model $F'(A)$, are determined by

$f_1(00, 0) = 01,$	$f_2(00, 0) = 10,$	$f_3(00, 1) = 00,$	$f_4(00, 1) = 11$
$f_5(01, 0) = 00,$	$f_6(01, 0) = 11,$	$f_7(01, 1) = 01,$	$f_8(01, 1) = 10$
$f_9(10, 0) = 11,$	$f_{10}(10, 0) = 00,$	$f_{11}(10, 1) = 10,$	$f_{12}(10, 1) = 01$
$f_{13}(11, 0) = 01,$	$f_{14}(11, 0) = 10,$	$f_{15}(11, 1) = 11,$	$f_{16}(11, 1) = 00$

For every z, $z \in \{00, 01, 10, 11\}$ and for every $x \in \{0, 1\}$ for which we have

$$z' = f_{i, j}(z, x) \neq z'' = f(z, x), \qquad i \in \{1, \ldots, 11, \text{in}\}, j \in \{0, 1\}$$

there exists a function f_k, $k \in \{1, \ldots, 16\}$ such that we have

$$z' = f_k(z, x) \neq z'' = f(z, x)$$

Thus the error model $F'(A)$ will determine the same error detection circuit of the Gray-code counter as $F(A)$. The assumed faults (single stuck-at-0/1 faults of the outputs of the elements $1, \ldots, 11$ and of the input line) can be modelled by the simple functional error model of single-bit errors of the state transition of the automata of the error model.

Remove the inverter gate 11 and connect the output of the inverter 1 to the second input of the gate 10. If the output of gate 1 is stuck-at-0/1 we have, for $A_{1,0}$,

$$z_1' = \bar{z}_2 \wedge x$$
$$z_2' = z_1 \wedge x \tag{A.8}$$

and, for $A_{1,1}$,

$$z_1' = z_1 \vee \bar{z}_2 \wedge x$$
$$z_2' = z_1 \wedge x \vee z_2 \tag{A.9}$$

The state diagrams of $A_{1,0}$ and $A_{1,1}$ are shown in Fig. A.12. In the state diagram of $A_{1,0}$ a functional 2-bit error, $f_{1,0}(11, 0) = 00$, instead of $f(11, 0) = 11$ occurs. This state transition is shown by a thick line in Fig. A.12. This functional error will not always be detected immediately by the error detection circuit determined by using the error model $F'(A)$. However, there is a high probability that the error 'A_{10} is implemented instead of A' will be detected.

If the invertor 11 is removed and if we demand that every single stuck-at-0/1 fault of the outputs of the elements 1 to 10 and of the input 12 has to be detected immediately by the error detection circuit, the error model $F'(A) = \{A_0, A_1, \ldots, A_{16}\}$ has to be completed by A_{17}:

$$f_{17}(z, x) = \begin{cases} 00 & \text{for } z = 11 \text{ and } x = 0 \\ f(z, x) & \text{otherwise} \end{cases}$$

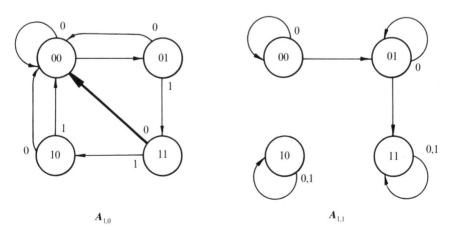

Figure A.12 Automata $A_{1,0}$ and $A_{1,1}$ of the error model; $A_{1,0}$ contains a 2-bit error, represented by the thick line.

REFERENCES

Aksenova, G.P. and E.S. Sogomonyan (1971) Synthesis of Built-in Test Circuits for Automata with Memory, *Automation and Remote Control*, vol. 32, no. 9, pp. 1492–1500.

Aksenova, G.P. and E.S. Sogomonyan (1975) Design of Self-Checking Built-in Check Circuits for Automata with Memory, *Automation and Remote Control*, vol. 36, no. 7, pp. 1169–1177.

Akushskij, I.J. and D.I. Juditzkij (1968) *Computer-Arithmetics in Residual Classes* (in Russian), Sovj. Radio, Moscow.

Anderson, D.A. and G. Metze (1973) Design of Totally Self-Checking Check Circuits for *m*-out-of-*n* Codes. *IEEE Trans. Comp.*, vol. C-22, pp. 263–269.

Anonymous (1983) Ein Vierteljahrhundert Informationsverarbeitung in Karlsruhe. *Elektronische Rechenanlagen*, vol. 25, pp. 157.

Arlat, J. and W.C. Carter (1984) Implementation and Evaluation of a (b,k)—Adjacent Error—Correcting Detecting Scheme for Supercomputer Systems, *IBM J. Res. Dev.*, vol. 28, no. 2, pp. 159–169.

Barsi, F. and P. Maestrini (1973) Error Correction Properties of Redundant Residue Number Systems, *IEEE Trans. Comp.*, vol. C-22, pp. 307–315.

Baugh, Ch.R. and B.A. Wooley (1975) Threshold Logic Circuit for Detecting Exactly *m* out of a Set of *n* Signals, US Pat. 3898616, GO6F 11/08.

Bennetts, R.G. (1984) *Design of Testable Logic Circuits*, Addison-Wesley, London.

Berdard, J.F. and V.C. Jaswa (1987) Self-Checking Digital Fault Detector for Modular Redundant Real Time Clock, US Pat. 468 3570, GO6F 11/18.

Berglund, N.L. (1979) Level-Sensitive Scan Design (LSSD), Tests, Chips, Boards, Systems, *Electronics*, vol. 52, pp. 108–110.

Bernstein, H. (1985) Doppelbit-Fehler, Erkennung und Beseitigung in byte-breiten RAM-Systemen, *Elektronik Industrie, Heidelberg*, vol. 16, no. 4, pp. 148, 152, 154.

Betrand, J.C., N. Gambiasi and J.J. Mercier (1974) Totally Self Checking Sequential Circuits, *Proceedings International Symposium on Discrete Systems*, Riga, Zinatne, vol. 2, pp. 36–44.

Biswas, N.N. (1984) Computer Aided Minimization Procedure for Boolean Functions, *Proceedings of 21st Design Automaton Conference*, pp. 699–702, Albuquerque, New Mexico.

Borisow, V.S. (1984) Fault Detecting and Correction in Memories (in Russian), *Radioelektronika, Moscow*, vol. 37, pp. 24–44.

Bossen, D.C. (1970) *b*-Adjacent Error Correction, *IBM J. Res. Dev.*, vol. 14, pp. 402–408.

Breuer, M.A. and A.D. Friedman (1976) *Diagnosis and Reliable Design of Digital Systems*, Computer Science Press, Woodland Hills.

Bryce, H. (1984) Chips Takes Only 40 ns to Find 1 Wrong Bit in 32 Bit Words, *Electronic Design*, vol. 32, no. 10, p. 267.

Carter, W.C. and P.R. Schneider (1968) Design of Dynamically Checked Computers, *Proceedings of IFIP Congress*, pp. 878–883.

Carter W.C., C. Ridgefield and P.P. Schneider (1971) Self Checking Error Checker for Parity Coded Data, US Pat. 360 2886, HO3K 13/34.

Case, P.W. (1981) Design Automation in IBM, *IBM J. Res. Dev.*, vol. 25, pp. 631–646.

Cavanagh, J. (1984) *Digital Computer Arithmetic*, McGraw-Hill, New York.

Cheng, W.T. and J.H. Patel (1984) Concurrent Error Detection in Iterative Logic Arrays, *Proceedings of 14th International Symposium on Fault Tolerant Computing*, pp. 10–15.

Christensen, B.A. (1975) Checking Circuit for a 1-out-of-N Decoder, US Pat. 388 6520, GO6F 11/08.

Criswell, P.B. (1985) Method and Means for Checking Normalizing Operations in a Computer Device, US Pat. 452 8640, GO6F 11/00.

Dadajev, Ju.G. (1981) *Theory of Arithmetic Codes* (in Russian), Radio i Svjas, Moscow.

Danilov, W.W. and A.N. Shibarok (1986) Toward a Theory of Functional Testing in Discrete Dynamic Systems, *Automation and Remote Control*, vol. 47, no. 12, pp. 1684–1691.

Danilov, W.W., N.W. Kolesov and E.P. Podkopajev (1975) An Algebraic Model for the Hardware Monitoring of Automata, *Automation and Remote Control*, vol. 36, no. 6, pp. 984–991.

Darringer, J.A. (1984) LSS. A System for Production Logic Synthesis, *IBM J. Res Dev.*, vol. 38, pp. 537–545.

Davis, R.H. and J.S. Harris (1971) Data Processing System, US Pat. 357 9200, GO6F 11/08.

Derbunowitsch, L.W. and W.W. Neshwejew (1986) Designing Completely Self-Testing Control Circuits Using Programmable Logic Arrays, *Automation and Remote Control*, vol. 47, no. 4, pp. 568–574.

Dhawan, S. and R.C. de Vries (1988) Design of Self-Checking Sequential Machines, *IEEE Trans. Comp.*, vol. C-37, pp. 1280–1315.

Diaz, M. (1974) Design of Totally Self Checking and Fail-Safe-Sequential Machines, *IEEE International Symposium on Fault Tolerant Computing*, pp. 19–24, Champaign.

Diaz, M., J.C. Geffroy and M. Courvoisier (1974) On-Set-Realization of Fail-Safe-Sequential Machines, *IEEE Trans. Comp.*, vol. C-23, pp. 133–138.

Efstathiou, C.C. and C. Halatsis (1983) Modular Realization of Totally Self Checking Checkers for m-out-of-n-Codes, *13th International Symposium on Fault Tolerant Computing*, Milano, pp. 154–161.

Eglauer, A. (1985) Fehlererkennung und -korrektur in Halbleiter-speichern, *Elektronik, München*, vol. 34, no. 15, pp. 53–58.

Etzel, M.H. and W.K. Jenkins (1980) Redundant Residue Number Systems for Error Detection and Correction in Digital Filters, *IEEE Trans. Acoust. Speech and Signal Processing*, vol. ASSP-28, pp. 538–544.

Flinders, M. *et al.* (1972) Error-Detecting Circuitry. US Pat. 364 6516, GO6F 11/00.

Fujiwara, E. and D.K. Pradhan (1990) Error Control Coding in Computers, *Computer Magazine*, vol. 23, no. 7, pp. 63–72.

Fujiwara, E., N. Muto and K. Matsuoka (1984) A Self-Testing Group-Parity Prediction Checker and Its Use for Built-in-Testing, *IEEE Trans. Comp.*, vol. C-33, pp. 578–583.

Fujiwara, H. (1985) *Logic Testing and Design for Testability*, MIT Press, Cambridge, Mass.

Fujiwara, W. (1983) A Self-Testing Group Parity Prediction Checker and Its Use for Built-in Testing, *13th International Symposium Fault Tolerant Computing*, Milano, pp. 146–153.

Fulton, J.M. (1971) Apparatus for Parity Checking a Binary Register, US Pat. 356 7916, GO6F 11/08.

Geisselhardt, W. (1978) Fehlerdiagnose in Geräten der Digital-technik, Hanser Verlag, Müchen.

Gill, A. (1962) *Introduction to the Theory of Finite State Machines*, McGraw-Hill, New York.

Gill, A. (1966) *Linear Sequential Circuits*, McGraw-Hill, New York.

Golomb, S.W. (1982) *Shift Register Sequences*, Aegean Park Press, Laguna Hills, CA.

Gössel, M. (1972) *Angewandte Automatentheorie*, vol. 2, *Lineare Automaten und Schieberegister*, Akademie-Verlag, Berlin.

Gössel, M. (1982) *Nonlinear Time-Discrete Systems (A General Approach by Nonlinear Superposition)*, Akademie-Verlag and Springer-Verlag, Berlin.

Gössel, M. (1991a) Optimal Error Detection Circuits for Sequential Circuits with Observable States. *Proceedings of 5th International Conference on Fault-Tolerant Computing Systems*, M. Dal Cin and W. Hohl (eds), Informatik-Fachberichte 283, pp. 171–180, Springer-Verlag, Berlin.

Gössel, M. (1991b) *Automatentheorie für Ingenieure*, Akademie-Verlag, Berlin.

Gössel, M. and B. Rebel (1984) On-line Fehlererkenung mit dem verallgemeinerten Superpositionsprinzip, *Nachrichten-technik-Elektronik*, vol. 34, pp. 27–29.

Gössel, M. and E.S. Sogomonyan (1993) A new self-testing and self-checking comparator (in preparation).

Graf, S., M. Gössel, B. Rebel and H. Schönyan (1984) Fehler-erkennungsschaltung, DD Pat. GO6F 11/16.

Hahn, W. and M. Gössel (1991) Pseudoduplication of Floating-Point Addition—A Method of Compiler Generated Checking of Permanent Hardware Faults, *Proceedings of 1991 IEEE VLSI Test Symposium*, pp. 161–165, Atlantic City.

Harrison, M.A. (1965) *Introduction to Switching and Automata Theory*, McGraw-Hill, New York.

Hartmanis, J. and R. Stearns (1966) *The Algebraic Structure Theory of Sequential Machines*, Prentice-Hall, Englewood Cliffs, N.J.

Hartung, M.H., R.E. Rieck and G.E. Tayler (1984) Method and Apparatus for Verifying Storage Apparatus Addressing, US Pat. 443 8512, GO6F 11/00.

Hellwagner, H. (1986) A Fault Detection Method in Partially Utilized Cellular (Systolic) Arrays, *Proceedings of Parcella 86*, Mathematical Research 29, pp. 138–146, Akademie-Verlag, Berlin.

Heltzig, H.F. and E. Oberst (1973) PRIMFIX—ein flexibler Algorithmus zur Ermittlung von Primkonjunktionen, *Messen-Steuern-Regeln*, vol. 16, pp. 32–36.

Hong, S., J. (1972) Error Detecting Circuit for Decoders, US Pat. 369 3152, HO3K 13/34.

Hong, Se.J., D.S. Jones and D.L. Ostapko (1973) Error Checking Circuit, US Pat. 376 4788, GO6F 11/00.

Hörbst, E., M. Nett and H. Schwärtzel (1986) VENUS-Entwurf von VLSI-Schaltungen, Springer-Verlag, Berlin.

Horwarth, J. (1985) Checking Sequential Logic Circuits, US Pat. 455 6976, GO6F 11/00.

Hsiao, M.Y., A.M. Patel and D.K. Pradhan (1977) Storage Address Generator with On-line Fault-Detection Capability, *IEEE Trans. Comp.*, vol. C-26, pp. 1144–1147.

Huang, C.H. (1983) A Fully Parallel Mixed-Radix Conversation Algorithm for Residue Number Applications, *IEEE Trans. Comp.* vol. C-32, pp. 398–402.

Jackowski, S.P. and J. Moyer (1985) Interface Checking Apparatus, US Pat. 456 1094, GO6 F 11/00.

Jarwala, N. and D.K. Pradhan (1987) Cost Analysis of On Chip Fault Tolerant Dynamic RAM's, *Proceedings of 17th IEEE International Symposium on Fault Tolerant Computing*, Pittsburg, Pa., pp. 278–282.

Jenkins, W.K. (1983) The Design of Error Checkers for Self-Checking Residue Number Arithmetic, *IEEE Trans. Comp.*, vol. C-32, pp. 388–396.

Jenkins, W.K. and E.J. Altman (1983) Residue Number System Error Checking Using Expanded Projections, *1983 IEEE International Symposium on Circuits and Systems*, Newport Beach, Calif., vol. 2, pp. 698–700.

Jessep, D.C. (1971) Fail-Safe Decoder Circuits, US Pat. 358 5377, HO3K 13/34.

Koch, K. and M. Nett (1984) CAD für IC, Data report 19, pp. 20–23.

Kohavi, Z. (1978) *Switching and Finite Automata Theory*, McGraw-Hill, New York.

Kulisch, U. (1976) *Grundlagen des numerischen Rechnens: math. Begründung der Rechnerarithmetik*, Bibliographisches Institut, Mannheim.

Kundu, S. and S.M. Reddy (1990) Embedded Totally Self-checking Checkers: A Practical Design, *IEEE Des. Test of Computers*, August 1990, pp. 5–16.

Laha, S. and J.H. Patel (1983) Error Correction in Arithmetic Operations Using Time Redundancy, *13th International Symposium on Fault Toletrant Computing*, Milano, pp. 198–305.

Lala, P.K. (1985) *Fault Tolerant and Fault Testable Hardware Design*, Prentice-Hall, Englewood Cliffs, N.J.

Langdon, G.G. and C.K. Tang (1970) Concurrent Error Detection for Group Look-Ahead Binary Adders, *IBM J. Res. Dev.*, vol. 14, pp. 563–573.

Larsen, R.W. and I.S. Reed (1972) Redundancy by Coding Versus Redundancy by Replication for Failure-Tolerant Sequential Circuits, *IEEE Trans. Comp.*, vol. C-21, pp. 130–137.

Lee, R.C. (1984) Fault and Error Detection Arrangement, US Pat. 442 9391, GO6F 11/10.

Litikov, J.J. and E.S. Sogomonyan (1985) Test and Functional Diagnosis of Digital Devices and Systems, *Automation and Remote Control*, vol. 46, no. 3, pp. 375–384.

McClellan, H.H. and C.M. Rader (1979) *Number Theory in Digital Signal Processing*, Prentice-Hall, Englewood Cliffs, N.J.

McPherson, A.F. (1973) Data Processor Sequence Checking Circuitry, US Pat. 371 3095, GO6F 11/00.

Mandelbaum, D. (1972) Error Correction in Residue Arithmetic, *IEEE Trans. Comp.*, vol. C-21, pp. 538–542.

Mauck, P. (1983) Rechnergestützter Entwurf integrierter Schaltungen, *Informatik-Fachberichte*, vol. 34, pp. 92–103, Springer Verlag, Berlin.

Maznew, V.I. (1977) Synthesis of Totally Self-Checking Sequential Circuits, *Automation and Remote Control*, vol. 38, no. 6, pp. 913–920.

Mercer, M.R. (1980) Digital Design for Testability and Concurrent Fault Detection in LSI and VLSI Devices, PhD Diss., University of Texas at Austin.

Mercer, M.R. (1986) Universally Testable Logic Element and Method for Structural Testing of Logic Circuits Formed of Such Logic Elements, US Pat. 462 5310, GO1R 31/28.

Meyer, J.F. and R.J. Sunderstrom (1975) On-Line Diagnosis of Unrestricted Faults, *IEEE Trans. Comp.*, vol. C-24, pp. 468–475.

Minero, R.H., A.J. Anello, R.G. Furey and L.R. Palounek (1972) Checking by Pseudoduplication, US Pat. 366 0646, GO6F 11/00.

Nagamo, G. and M. Takahahi (1983) Error Correction System, US Pat. 439 4763, GO6F 11/10.

Nauya, T. and Y. Toma (1983) A 3 Lines Realization of Totally Self Checking Checkers for *m*-out-of-*n* Codes. *Proceedings of 13th International Symposium on Fault Tolerant Computing*, Milano, pp. 173–176.

Newton, A.R., *et al.* (1981) Design Aids for VLSI: The Berkeley Perspective, *IEEE Trans., Circ. Syst.*, vol. CS-28, pp. 666–680.

Nicolaides, M. (1989) Self-Exercising Checkers for Unified Built-in Selftest (UBIST), *IEEE Trans. Computer-Aided Des.*, vol. 8, pp. 203–218.

Nigmatullin, R.G. (1983) *Complexity of Boolean Functions* (in Russian), Izd. Kaz. Un., Kazan.

Niraj, J.J. and J.A. Abraham (1984) The Design of Totally Self Checking Embedded Checkers. *14th International Symposium on Fault Tolerant Computing*, pp. 265–270.

Oberst, E. (1975) Theorie und Technik der Minimierung von Kombinationsschaltungen auf der Basis der Normalformentheorie, Diss. B, TU Dresden.

Olah, G. (1973) Computer Checking System, US Pat. 374 5316, GO6F 11/00.

Parchomenko, P.P. and E.S. Sogomonyan (1981) *Fundamentals in Technical Diagnostics* (in Russian), Energoisdat, Moscow.

Parekhij, R.A., G. Venkatesh and S.D. Sherlekar (1991) A Methodology for Designing Optimal Self-Checking Sequential Circuits. *Proceedings of 1991 International Test Conference*, pp. 283–291, Nashville.

Patel, J.H. and L.Y. Fung (1982) Concurrent Error Detection in ALU's by Recomputing with Shifted Operands, *IEEE Trans. Comp.*, vol. C-31, pp. 589–595.

Patel, J.H. and L.Y. Fung (1983) Concurrent Error Detection in Multiply and Divide Arrays, *IEEE Trans. Comp.*, vol. C-32, pp. 417–422.

Peterson, J.E. (1983) Method and an Arrangement for Supervising Faults when Transmitting Data between Computers, US Pat. 439 0989, GO6F 11/10.

Peterson, W.W. and E.J. Weldon (1972) *Error Correcting Codes*, MIT Press, Cambridge, Mass.

Piestra, K.S. (1983) Design Method of Totally Self Checking Checkers for *m*-out-of-*n*-Codes, *Proceedings of 13th International Symposium on Fault Tolerant Computing*, Milano, pp. 162–168.

Pilz, S. (1984) Methodik und Technologie des rechnergestützten Entwurfes elektronischer Geräte, *Messen-Steuern-Regeln*, vol. 27, pp. 114–122.

Powell, W.C. (1973) Error Detecting Circuit, US Pat. 371 0318, HO3K 13/32.

Pradhan, D.K. (ed.) (1986) *Fault-Tolerant Computing*, Prentice-Hall, Englewood Cliffs, N.J.

Pradhan, D.K. and S.M. Reddy (1973) Fault Tolerant Asynchronous Networks, *IEEE Trans. Comp.*, vol. C-22, pp. 662–669.

Procter, B.J. (1985) Data Processing System, US Pat. 450 7784, GO6F 11/00.

Proto, R.C. (1978) Apparatus for Verifying the Execution of a Sequence of Coded Instructions, US Pat. 410 8359, GO6F 11/08.

Rao, T.R.N. (1974) *Error Coding for Arithmetic Processors*, Academic Press, New York.

Rao, T.R.N. and E. Fujiwara (1989) *Error Control Coding for Computer Systems*, Prentice-Hall, New York.

Raymond, T.C. (1981) LSI/VLSI-Design Automation, *Computer*, vol. 14, pp. 89–101.

Reed, I.S. and A.C.L. Chiang (1970) Coding Techniques for Failure Tolerant Counters, *IEEE Trans. Comp.*, vol. C-19, pp. 1035–1038.

Reitwieser, G.W. (1960) Binary Arithmetic, in *Advances in Computers*, vol. 1, pp. 231–308.

Roth, J.P. (1980) *Computer Logic Testing and Verification*, Computer Science Press, Pontomac, Md.

Saposhnikov, W.W. and W. Saposhnikov (1984) *Discrete Automatons with Fault Detection* (in Russian), Energoatomisdat, Leningrad.

Sawin, D.H. (1975) Design of Reliable Synchronous Sequential Circuits, *IEEE Trans. Comp.*, vol. C-24, pp. 567–570.

Sedmak, R.M. (1979) Design for Self-Verification. An Approach for Dealing with Testability Problems in VLSI-based Design, *Proceedings of 1979 IEEE Test Conference*, pp. 112–120.

Sellers, F.F., M.J. Hsiao and L.W. Bearnson (1968) *Error Detecting Logic for Digital Computers*, McGraw-Hill, New York.

Siewiorek, D.P. and R.S. Schwarz (1982) *The Theory and Practice of Reliable System Design*, Digital Press, Bedford.

Smith, W.W. (1980) System for Detecting and isolating Static Bit Faults in a Network of Arithmetic Units, US Pat. 418 1969, G06F 11/00.

Sogomonyan, E.S. (1970) The Design of Discrete Devices with Diagnostics in the Course of Operation, *Automation and Remote Control*, vol. 31, no. 11, pp. 1854–1860.

Sogomonyan, E.S. (1981) Design of Single-Output Self-Checking Check Circuits, *Automation and Remote Control*, vol. 42, no. 3, part 2, pp. 3–10.

Sogomonyan, E.S. and M. Gössel (1992) Self-Testing and Self-Checking Combinational Circuits with Weakly Independent Outputs, *Proceedings of 10th IEEE VLSI Test Symposium*, Atlantic City, pp. 298–303.

Sogomonyan, E.S. and E.V. Slabakov (1989) *Self-testing Circuits and Fault Tolerant Systems* (in Russian), Radio i Svjas, Moscow.

Speranskij, D.V. (1985) On United Circuits for Functional Diagnosis and Test for Discrete Systems, *Automation and Remote Control*, vol. 46, no. 1, part 2, pp. 106–109.

Stodola, K.C. (1982) Data Bus Fault Detector, US Pat. 432 8583, GO6F 11/00.

Swoboda, J. (1973) *Codierung zur Fehlerkorrektur und Fehlererkennung*, Oldenburg-Verlag, München.

Szabo, N.S. and R.I. Tanaka (1967) *Residue Arithmetics and Its Application to Computer Technology*, McGraw-Hill, New York.

Takaoka, T. and T. Ibaraki (1972) N-fail-safe Sequential Machines, *IEEE Trans. Comp.*, vol. C-21, pp. 1189–1196.

Taylor, J.M. (1984) Paritätsprüfschaltung für ein binär zählendes Register, DE Pat. 253 6625, H03K 13/32.

Thoma, Y., Y. Ohyama and R. Sakai (1971) Realization of Fail-Safe Sequential Machines by Using a k-out-of-n Code, *IEEE Trans. Comp.*, vol. C-20, pp. 1270–1275.

Tomlin, J.J. (1970) Error Detector for Frequency Changers, US Pat. 354 8175, HO3K 13/32.

Trautwein, M. (1984) Concurrent Error Detection—Correction of Logical Operations, in *Fehlertolerierende Rechnersysteme*, K.E. and M. Dal Cin (eds), 2te GI/NTG/GMR-Fachtagung, Herausg. Großpietsch, pp. 190–201, Springer-Verlag, Berlin.

Umo, M. and M. Ikuro (1980) Diagnostic Check System for Digital Signal Circuits, US Pat. 420 0225, GO1R 31/28.

Wakerly, J.F. (1974) Partially Self Checking Circuits and Their Use in Performing Logical Operations, *IEEE Trans. Comp.*, vol. C-23, pp. 658–666.

Wakerly, J.F. (1978) *Error Detecting Codes, Self-Checking Circuits and Applications*, North-Holland, New York.

Wing, N.T. and E. Glen (1982) Self Checking Arithmetic Unit, US Pat. 431 4350, GO6F 11/14.

Willmaun, K. (1984) Fehlererkennung und -korrektur mit dem 32-Bit-EDAC SN 74ALS 632, *Elektronik Industrie, Heidelberg*, vol. 15, no. 11, pp. 130–133.

Wunderlich, H.J. (1991) *Hochintegrierte Schaltungen: Prüfgerechter Entwurf und Test*, Springer-Verlag, Berlin.

Zander, H.J. (1982) *Logischer Entwurf binärer Systeme*, VEB Verlag Technik, Berlin.

Ziegler, M.I., M.B. Druke, R.R. Rockel and W. Baxter (1983) Refresh and Error Detection and Correction Technique for a Data Processing System, US Pat. 438 0812, GO6F 11/10.

Zola, M.J. (1974) Self Checking Decoder, US Pat. 378 4978, HO3K 13/34.

INDEX